Contact: Taylor Made Publishing, LLC
Attn: R.M. Shiver
PO Box 861
Greenville, NC 27835
www.taylormadenc.com

Although inspired by some real-life situations, this tale, in its entirety, is a work of fiction. All references to characters, online comments, newspaper articles, emails and other pseudo-facts indicated, implied or suggested from media sources are coincidental. All characters created are imaginary.

"A day will come when the story inside you will want to breathe on its own. That's when you'll start writing." --Sarah Noffke

I suppose that happened to me when certain shattering events transpired during the latter part of my career in government when many observers saw dreams die in terms of expectations for a successful career in public service for the female population in Kinder County. The setting could have been Any County, USA, but the episodes described in the chapters that follow took place in a make-believe coun- ty known as Kinder County in the State of Xenolina somewhere in the universe.

KINDER COUNTY

Kinder County is a beautiful picturesque area of small towns and rural villages, covering roughly 870 square miles. It is really divided into three territories---the east, the central, and the west. In the early 1900s the landscape held many Chinaberry trees—almost one in every backyard. According to research, the Chinaberry tree was introduced as an ornamental specimen to the United States in 1930 and became the aesthetic landscape choice in the southern United States. It wasn't long before southern families discovered that these trees held great medicinal value and, thus, families began using these trees for medicinal purposes. This was during a period in history where very few families had access to medical care. During this period of time, the population of Kinder County was less than 10,000. Today, the population has reached 70,000, and the landscape is peppered with mobile home parks on much of the land that was used years ago for farming.

The people of Kinder County, for the most part, are friendly, easygoing, and hard-working. Mon- day through Friday they are engaged in some type of work, either within the boundaries of Kinder County or in surrounding counties via commutes. Saturday is the day for shopping, recreation of some form, dating, and dinner engagements. On Sundays you will find many of its citizens in a church of the religious denomination of their choice.

Kinder County residents, much like the people of many southern towns and along the countryside where life is good and the prevailing lifestyle is easygoing and laid back, often are drawn to gossip, more so as a form of entertainment and engaging conversations rather than with any malicious intent—for the most part. It has been through numerous friendships and community networks that a great deal of insight has been gained, enabling the accumulation of an arsenal of fictitious ammunition in the form of tales and stories that help make up the contents of this psuedo-exposition. Tremendous gratitude is given to all contributing friends, frenemies, and acquaintances who wanted to see a document featuring a story that highlights the good, the bad, and the ugly of Kinder County in order to educate our neighbors

5

across the State of Xenolina, and perhaps even our great nation, about experiences of powerless employees and citizens as they continue to exist currently in small-town workforces, but where most victims are too busy themselves to compile and construct an eye-opening revelation.

The average annual temperature of Kinder County is 65 degrees and the average annual rainfall is conducive to farming. The combination of mild temperatures and moderate rainfall make Kinder County a perfect place for farming. As a result, there are many thriving farms that remain operational throughout the county. Farming families grow large crops of corn, peanuts, beans, and dewberries. Dewberries are so plentiful that a few years ago Kinder County citizens were inclined to organize a Dewberry Festival. This festival takes place annually in the month of July. People come from all four corners of the State of Xenolina to join the festivities. Activities range from 5K runs, a dewberry pancake breakfast, assorted art displays from local artists, crafts, dancing, clogging, big band shows, plant sales, and an assortment of dewberry dishes prepared by locals and presented for connoisseurs to judge and show favor.

Among the great assets of Kinder County is that its eastern-most side borders the ocean, creating both a beautiful landscape and a place of recreation for beach-goers and water lovers. While most of its shoreline is undeveloped, there are a few dotted spots harboring a pier, a small park, and several developing towns. The mayor, Zack Russ, of one of the towns, is one of the most visionary individuals Kinder County has ever known. He is loved by the people and strongly supported by his town's council. For these two reasons alone, he has been able to create a broad expansion of commerce and beach activities capable of matching even small towns on the coast of California. There are sprawling beach homes and condos designed for addressing a diverse population, while at the same time laid out to accommodate continuous growth.

Of course, growth and development have a lot to do with good leadership. And Kinder County has been deprived of good leadership since the present governing board, the "Coterie," took over and began to smother county progress because its members are more interested in advancing their personal agendas.

THE COTERIE

The Coterie is a group of elected and appointed officials who govern Kinder County, not by
rules established under Federal and State laws, but by
their own warped whims, non-institutional be- liefs,
and tawdry capricious ideas. The Coterie could be
compared to a kleptocracy, a government where
kleptocrats *"use their power to exploit the people... in
order to extend their personal wealth and polit- ical
power. Kleptocracies are generally associated with
dictatorships, oligarchies, military juntas, or other
forms of autocratic and nepotist governments in
which external oversight is impossible or does not
exist."* Being subjected to this style of governing, any
unexplainable events might occur on any given day in
Kinder County government. And, unfortunately,
Kinder County employees, foot soldiers who   ensure

that daily essential functions of public service are performed, are often victimized by this frivolously operating style of local government. It should be pointed out that Kinder County did not always operate under the current rulers and their unorthodox style.

Kinder County, at one time, operated in a manner that brought a sense of pride to its citizenry and employees. Federal regulations were followed; state rules and regulations were honored; all employees were respected for the difficult tasks they performed daily; and employees, for the most part, were treat- ed fairly. But those days are bygone days for Kinder County Government.

Today, the Coterie rules by fear and intimidation, and anyone who is fearless or not intimidated by their antics find themselves harassed overtly or covertly, and eventually terminated from employment without justifiable cause. The only way to avoid this imposed sentence is to resign, find other employment, or retire.

The question doesn't need to be asked whether or not the Coterie is a body or entity that's difficult to work for. All one has to do is consider the fact that every two or three years the Coterie is changing County Keepers. The Coterie uses treacherous and intimidating tactics behind closed doors in closed sessions. A

County Keeper doesn't even have the opportunity to move forward with any special projects, or make any progressive moves for Kinder County before the Coterie is sending him or her packing.

This doesn't happen in surrounding counties and other counties throughout the State of Xenolina. Other County Keepers are able to plan and execute great ideas for the people of their respective coun-ties and implement grand and positive changes that are congruent with growth over the years. But not in Kinder County. If a County Keeper in Kinder County proposes a new idea and Servicious, Kinder County's dictator, doesn't see where he can personally benefit from it, the idea is squashed, and in a fit of one of his tantrums, Servicious invites the County Keeper to resign or have his employment terminated. So Kinder County has suffered a turnover of County Keepers at an unprecedented rate. In fact, Redhawk, the protagonist of this story who served as Kinder County Department of Alliance Activity (DAA) Director had the privilege of serving under 25 different County Keepers during a 33-year period. Imagine that?

Considering the instability under which County Keepers perform in Kinder County, it is miraculous that Redhawk lasted as DAA for more than 30 years. But that's because in the midst of all the turmoil, there were always some loyal, dedicated Department

Keepers, and genuinely enthusiastic highly qualified staff that were always determined to give the public quality service. And over the 33 years, there had been many Coterie members and County Keepers who had the people's best interest and Kinder County's growth and well-being in the forefront of governing.

Kinder County, in the past, had previously hired several County Keepers, James Bond and Rock Boston, who at least understood the ramifications of frivolous spending and thus acted conservatively to keep the county on solid ground, while at the same time taking steps to keep the county moving forward into the 21st Century.

Yet, while the progressive County Keepers acted to move Kinder County forward, in the pro- cess they often neglected Kinder County employees, the foot soldiers responsible for the day-to-day op- erations of programs, and the service-deliverers who sacrifice family time for unpaid overtime to ensure that Kinder County citizens receive benefits and ser- vices that they are in need of and entitled to receive. Services are delivered timely, accurately, respectfully, and compassionately by employees, with little or no appreciation from the Coterie. One of the Coterie's favorite expressions with reference to Kinder Coun- ty employees is, "They had better be glad they have a job!" And this has been the prevailing attitude for years.

When some departments put forth efforts to improve morale, the Coterie frowns upon the activities, even though employees are operating at their own personal expenses and on their own earned time.

One would think that for the Coterie to profess that one of its goals is to achieve a high-performing organization, it would do more to boost the morale of the dedicated employees who loyally serve the pub-lic on a daily basis. But, instead, the Coterie only operates to appease its members and a few employees who Coterie members feel can do the most for the Coterie, its cohorts, and friends personally. One tenet that clearly defines the Coterie as it applies to the treatment of the majority of Kinder County employees is, "They don't eat their own cooking!" The vitriolic phrases that the Coterie uses to demean and desecrate certain Kinder County employees are never used when discussing Kinder County citizens who they feel can be used to benefit the Coterie covertly. It is no wonder that decent, intelligent, professional County Keepers don't bode well as drivers, operators, or conductors at the control in Kinder County.

The Coterie developed a small park in the *middle of nowhere*—away from growing communities inhabited by families with young children who could really benefit by having this facility close to their homes where it could be utilized. But due to the park's isolation, it is almost never utilized. One of the interesting points about the park's location—even though it is isolated from the hub of community activity where it could be readily utilized by Kinder County families and children—is it happens to be only a short distance from Servicious' home. This is just one of the prime examples of how the Coterie wastes tax dollars on their personal, insignificant pet projects.

SCHADEN

It was going to be a crazy election in November. Schaden had done everything ugly to everyone whom she felt has political clout. Then, when she really needed all the help she could get in order to retain her office, she didn't know whom she could trust. Probably *no one*. Because if you had abused people in the same manner she had, you wouldn't know whom to trust either. *You reap what you sow!*

During her reign, Schaden hooked up with the Millionaire whom she had pegged to help carry out her dirty deeds. She also planned to capitalize on the Millionaire's wealth by purchasing stocks in his multi-million dollar adventure. Schaden felt that this was a way for her to become funky rich in her old age since she had blown all opportunities to earn money the way honest, hard-working people do--by finishing high school, going to college, or learning a trade or special skills, going into the military, or joining the family business. Schaden was too smart for all that. She dropped out, and later, it is rumored, completed the GED. Whatever made her think that made her so smart truly escaped the rest of us. But she did think she was smarter, and in the end found that she had only out-smarted herself. Because in her old age when she should have been relaxing and enjoying the fruits of her youthful labor, she found that she was a poor, broke, bitter old hag.

Anyway, as it turns out, the Millionaire had grossly miscalculated his impending fortune. He had believed that he was about to gain $50 million in a short period of time through mining earthly minerals that he would sell to the state. His good friend and co-conspirator, Shaden, had assured him she had everything in the bag in terms of snowballing her big-time colleagues to award a contract to the Millionaire. He was counting on a building boom and the need for highways and street-paving, but the economy went "bust" and so did the anticipated building boom, leaving the Millionaire stuck with a lot of "big" bills. And where did that leave Schaden? After having scraped and borrowed every penny she could in order to invest in the Millionaire's big business venture, Schaden's status was reduced to low income. It must be a tremendous shock to fall from imaginary queen to near pauper in a matter of months. The Millionaire's colleagues didn't teach him *not to count his biddies before they hatched.* And, obviously, he had never been taught that you reap what you sow. And he must have forgotten that God is watching everything you do. Maybe if he had remembered, he would have had second thoughts before perpetrating any maltreatment against those whom he considered his underlings! Perhaps the Millionaire would have remembered that when he sat "high" and tried to deprive others for no reason other than *sheer envy.* Perhaps he would have remembered that people should be judged by the content of their character and respected and rewarded accordingly. Because if the Millionaire had listened, and remembered and judged accordingly, God would be smiling on him right now. No one wishes Mr. Millionaire ill will, but everyone knows that you can't do wrong things to God's children and expect everything to turn out right for you. *It just ain't going to happen*!

Getting back to Schaden, her tactics of abusing and harassing Hispanics and Latinos weren't going to boost *"what she hoped for"* and help her gain the world. She focused on trying to elevate her status by stepping on others. Just because she wasn't gaining in the stock market was no reason for her to denigrate the less fortunate. What if the *powers-that-be,* way back when, would have rounded up her ancestors like cattle and herded them back from whence they came? Perhaps she would be doing just as well as she is doing today. Or perhaps not, because she just doesn't seem to be doing very well these days. Even so, it could be worse. Nevertheless, she and her cohorts' mean spirits still overshadow any good that might be buried in their poor souls as they yearn for yesteryear's upper hand. *Poverty is humbling!* Schaden never imagined she would be in this fix, I am willing to bet. But everyone knows, *things happen*!

Why did some Kinder County folk see things only one way? For example, why did they not feel it's OK to let other people come to Kinder County the way their ancestors did? Some people didn't just come here; they imported other people from foreign lands and made servants of them. *It was so perplex- ing. Was there anyone who understood this phenomenon?* So what if they rounded up Hispanics and took them back to Mexico as Schaden had suggested? Who was going to perform all the services and do the work that was performed by that dedicated, energetic segment of the population? Were there replacement human resources who knew how to toil long hours in the hot sun? Why did you let all your corporate brothers take our jobs to other countries in search of more cheap labor!? *You just didn't quit, did you?*

SERVICIOUS

Schaden's other close cohort or partner in deception is the dictator Servicious. During his ear-ly childhood and formative years Servicious was a spoiled brat, and he has brought those bratty tendencies into his adult life. He, unknowingly, always shows the public his ugly side through his many snide remarks, sassy quips, and churlish and offensive demeanor. While others clearly discern his surly character, Servicious holds a false sense of pomposity that puts a bad taste in the mouths of those in his presence.

Servicious grew up to be fairly tall and somewhat imposing boy due to his beefy appearance. By some accounts he could have been described as handsome, but the ugliness of his character eclipsed that notion. He could be likened to today's young bullies, and the only difference today is Servicious is an older bully. He operates in attack mode and targets anyone who he feels might be a roadblock in his path of destruction. His attack on DAA Director Redhawk can be viewed as an attack on all Kinder County employees, whether direct or covert. Servicious will passionately go after anyone who disagrees with his agenda, the purpose of which is to put himself in a position equal to, and often above, God Almighty. No one is going to get in Servicious' way and prevent him from reaching this ultimate goal. In his narrow-minded way of thinking, any colleague or employee whom he consideres an adversary has to be destroyed by any means necessary. Redhawk was one such imagined enemy targeted by Servicious.

REDHAWK

Redhawk, a native of Kinder County, lived in the Hawk Town village, named in honor of her ancestors, the village founders. The track of land on which Redhawk lived was purchased in 1919 by Redhawk's grandfather, Hawkeye, son of Grateful. Hawkeye was tall, handsome, bronze, and had curly black hair, unlike the straight hair of his mother, Grateful. This deviation in hair texture, no doubt, occurred because Grateful's husband, Earl, was as black as midnight with hair as kinky as steel wool. *Genes somehow always tell the story very truthfully.* The road on which Redhawk lived was named Grateful Road in honor of the grand old lady herself.

Redhawk, a copper-toned female slightly above average height, inherited genes for hair texture from her great-grandfather Earl. She had no distinguishing physical features that would have caused her to be noticed when she entered a room. However, her reticence and reserved mannerism might have drawn attention to her in the midst of a rowdy crowd. Her dark eyes always spoke volumes if one were observant enough to read the message she conveyed through them. This aspect of her total characteristics followed her from childhood to the woman who morphed from a cocoon that had been shaped throughout her formative years by a loving family. Her tendency to be inconspicuously observant, coupled with her keen sense of hearing, enabled her to capture voluminous tidbits of interesting facts. This quality of her personality proved to be immeasurably significant later in her life as she embarked on a career that demanded her utmost attention.

MISS GRATEFUL

Miss Grateful, as she was called, was a tall, slender, graceful woman—bronze-skinned and beautiful by all standards of beauty. She wore her long, dark, silky hair in a single braid that hung like a rope down her back. Her footwear of choice was moccasins, and her daily attire always included an old fringed shawl, no matter what season it happened to be. She always wore ankle-length dresses and skirts, hiding a pair of gorgeous shapely legs that would be the envy of anyone who models legs for a living.

Old Lady Grateful, a proud Native American, was a woman of few words. But when she spoke, all seven of her sons listened and acted on her instructions. One primary point she preached to her sons was to purchase land and hold on to it because God would not be remaking the Earth and adding more land than presently exists. Because of her mantra and her son Hawkeye's obedience, three generations later Redhawk was the fortunate beneficiary who inherited the tract where her family currently resides.

In the days when Miss Grateful roamed the homestead tract, the landscape was vastly different. Miss Grateful had her personal garden down by the brook where years later Redhawk had a gazebo constructed. While Miss Grateful found a tremendous sense of peace working in the garden, Redhawk found it peaceful to sit in the gazebo and write. Redhawk and her great-grandmother, each in her own way, produced some special food. One produced food for the body, while the other produced food for thought.

HAWKEYE

Hawkeye was 22 years old when he was called to serve in the United States Army as the world became involved in war number one, known as the First World War (WWI). It began on July 28, 1914, and lasted four years, three months, and two weeks un- til Nov. 11, 1918. At the end of the war, because he had received serious injuries during battle, Hawkeye was honorably discharged with a disability pension. Having saved most of his soldier's salary, he returned home and honored his mother by purchasing a beautiful tract of land along the Northeast Cape Dread River. This is the tract of land that Redhawk, being the only known child of Hawkeye's only son, Kenhawk, would eventually inherit.

Redhawk was blessed as a child to have both paternal and maternal grandparents to love and care for her. She spent an enormous amount of time with each of them. This was easy due to the proximity of their homes. Only a two-mile stretch separated them. The distance between their two farms was an easy walk for the long-legged, hyperactive Redhawk, and she made the trek often.

Both of Redhawk's grandmothers had bibli- cal names—Mary and Hannah—and both were kind, loving, compassionate, industrious, God-fearing women. But while one grandmother was quiet and reserved, the other grandmother was ebullient, gregarious, and very outgoing. Both grandmothers lived on farms and not only maintained a household with many back-breaking duties, but they worked in the fields as well. So the Protestant ethic was scrupulously instilled in Redhawk early in life as these two impeccable women modeled great expectations for the bright and bubbly child.

HORATIO TRAYES

Redhawk's grandfathers were strong handsome men who also understood the value of hard work. Will Malloy, her maternal grandfather, worked as foreman for one of the richest men in the State of Xenolina, Horatio Trayes. Mr. Horatio, as he was fondly known, was one of the most gentle and generous men of his time. For being a great foreman and friend, Mr. Horatio gave Will Malloy lots of land holdings. This in turn created more work for Will Malloy's family, while Will himself was busy overseeing Mr. Horatio Trayes' farm.

Mr. Horatio's primary farm crop was beautiful flowers. There were daffodils, irises, buttercups, gladiolas, and gypsum. These flowers were shipped to large floral shops in the Northeast—New York, Philadephia, Connecticut, Rhode Island, Massachusetts, Maine, and others. There was a huge market for beautiful flowers during the 1940s and 1950s. Many local florists also benefited from the flowers grown on Mr. Horatio's flower farm.

During harvest season in the spring and early summer, as one looked around the villages of Hawktown and Dane's Ferry, there was great beauty to behold as huge fields burst forth with an array of bright colors creating rainbows on the ground. Sometimes travelers passing through the area would stop and stand in awe of the surrounding beauty.

Those flower fields provided jobs for all families in the area who were willing to and could work outside in the elements—blazing hot sun, rain, cold weather, all included. But Kinder County citizens who worked those fields considered it a blessing to have a place to work within walking distance of home because very few families could afford automobiles. It was also a blessing having Mr. Horatio as a boss, because he cared so much about the well-being of the families who worked for him and the functionality of their community.

Following in Mr. Trayes' footsteps years later, his son, Horatio Trayes Jr., would donate a large tract of land to build a local high school named in his family's honor.

GRANDFATHERS

And it was a blessing having Mr. Will, as Redhawk's grandfather was affectionately known, as Mr. Horatio's foreman. Mr. Will was a live wire—a bundle of energy who worked tirelessly—who toiled 12 to 14 hours daily, six, sometimes seven days a week. When Mr. Will wasn't working, he could be seen driving one of Mr. Horatio Trayes' work buses taking a group of happy kids to Bottomsail Beach. These trips to the beach were generally the highlight of many of the children's summer activity.

Observing these men as a young girl, Redhawk learned valuable lessons about how to treat and interact with people upon whose labor one depends in order to be successful. She secretly vowed to herself that when she grew up, if she were ever in a position to be boss over people, above all else, she would be kind, caring and compassionate, understanding, and fair. Because, through example, it was instilled in her how kindness and fairness are great motivators for maximizing production.

Redhawk's paternal grandfather, Hawkeye, was a truck farmer. He grew crops of corn, beans, peanuts, watermelons and cantaloupes, cucumbers, strawberries, and tobacco. He also had an orchard of pecan trees. Early on, Hawkeye taught Redhawk to be an entrepreneur. On hot summer days you would find her sitting beside the road under a pecan tree surrounded by lots of watermelons and other fruits and vegetables selling produce to eager customers. She was an apt child who loved being outdoors, so it was a great joy for her to be able to work as a mini-saleslady selling her granddaddy's cornucopia of fruits and vegetables from the fields. Hawkeye never failed to pay Redhawk a small allowance for having the time of her life interacting with the many customers—friends and neighbors—who dropped by for a small purchase, but mostly just to sit a while and chat. Redhawk was taught early on that a portion of the allowance was to be saved—in the words of her grandfather—for a rainy day. In the beginning she was too young to interpret the phrase because she thought it was meant literally. But as time passed, she clearly understood that it meant saving in case of an emergency. She learned that lesson well and adhered to it throughout her life.

KENHAWK

Kenhawk and Redhawk's mother, Daneechee, doted on their only child, and made sure that all of her basic needs were met. They taught her to live by the Golden Rule and to apply herself 100 percent to whatever endeavor she undertook. Redhawk was an outstanding student throughout all her years of studying. When she entered the work force it was with a deep passion to give every task her very best effort, and to meet every challenge with great vim and vigor. Anyone who observed her throughout her career as the DAA Director for Kinder County Government could see how diligently she worked at task completion, and the efforts she put forth in every assignment to ensure an accurate and excellent outcome.

Kenhawk was both a captivating and magnetic personality. He especially attracted the attention of females with his mellifluous voice and good looks. He was a gorgeous hunk of a man and, most importantly, he was a gentleman. He was respectful of others, kind and generous, and humble with an air of tranquility about him. That's not to say he wasn't fun-loving and puissant, because he was charismatically powerful in a business sense. Kenhawk tended the family farm and simultaneously was employed at International Paper Company. So he was never without income. He was debonair and adventuresome, and Redhawk always felt a sense of excitement in his presence.

DANEECHEE

Daneechee was the perfect mate for Kenhawk. She was a tall, lean, beautiful, robust woman with great inner strength. She had been born into a family that eventually grew to 13 children. And because of this, Daneechee was one of the most resourceful women of her time. Kenhawk and Daneechee fell in love and married in their early 20s. She was 20 and he was 23. One year after their union, Daneechee gave birth to a beautiful baby girl—Redhawk. From that day forward, Daneechee spent every waking hour catering to the baby girl's every whim. Daneechee was strong and energetic with the stamina necessary to handle running a household and taking care of a new baby.

Daneechee was a Social Worker before the title was applied to the profession, and before the very young Redhawk had ever heard the term. When not engaged in household chores or caring for little Redhawk, Daneechee spent her time assisting neighbors, running errands for them, and helping with other simple chores. She won the hearts of many children, and often their families, because she would give her last dollar to purchase shoes for a child's bare feet or food for families if they were hungry.

So this caring and giving spirit was all that Redhawk ever observed, and no doubt it was the impetus for Redhawk's choosing Social Work as her life-long profession. This family background was the root of her passion for working in a helping profession. Which makes it baffling, then, how Servicious, and his Coterie of bandoleros thought they could concoct a scheme in an attempt to destroy Redhawk's stellar record in the field of Human Services.

SERVICIOUS

It is quite possible that Servicious was envious of Redhawk's land holdings and that was one of the reasons, among many unknown others, that he put Redhawk under attack. But he should not have been envious of Redhawk's property because Servicious has land-holdings of his own. Some people just want it all and it seems that Servicious wanted to take Redhawk's inheritance. The question is "Why"? Maybe one day before the end of time that question will be answered.

One story goes like this. Servicious sets out to destroy Redhawk, a county employee who had been working for Kinder County for more than 20 years when Servicious joined the Coterie. Schaden and Servicious conspired to point out to the Coterie alleged "lies" that Rehawk had told relative to, and in preparation of, the 2011-2012 Budget.

This was offered as an excuse to reduce the budget in the Department of Alliance Activity in order to use funds from that department to cover other county business rather than dip into the general fund balance. Kinder County was facing more than a $250 million budget shortfall. However, as it turns out, Redhawk had not, I repeat *had not*, lied but had only presented facts. But you see, Servicious could not fully grasp the facts, so naturally he assumed that Redhawk was lying. So these two had another par- ty contact the Super Power, the State of Xenolina, to come down and explain and present the truth. The truth was painful and these guys were in denial, but they were going to have to provide services to the poor whether they liked it or not. The U. S. Constitution says, *"They shall"* and State laws say, *"They shall"*! The Xenolina official, Preston Lane, who appeared before the Kinder County Coterie validated that Redhawk's presentation and account of the DAA were accurate.

PRESTON LANE

One look at the business liaison who had been sent to provide an explanation and the Coterie knew that this tall, handsome, powerfully built guy was not going to tolerate their nonsense, but was going to give them the hard cold facts relative to their responsibility to the low-income citizens of Kinder County, whether they liked it or not. His soothingly low booming voice always delivered a message loaded with accurate facts. Having served the state Super Power in a financial capacity for many years where he used his keen accounting skills to check DAA agencies in counties throughout the State of Xenolina, he exuded great confidence relative to the subject matter because he was an expert in his field.

Ha! Ha! They thought they had finally lucked up on a reason to get rid of Redhawk, but that was not going to happen according to their plan. When Redhawk left Kinder County Government, it was going to be according to *her own personal plan!* Redhawk was right one more time. *God bless America!* Deep down, you know how people are, but hope that you are wrong. In the end, you discover that they are actually worse than you could have ever imagined. But their antics are bound to backfire sooner or later. Was Redhawk the only employee in Kinder County Government that had to be perfect? Many tales have been told about unethical acts by the so-called *crème de la crème* in the government. But that is fodder for a later chapter or another book. But let it just be said that Servicious was a dominator. He wanted to control everything and everybody. It has been stated that he suffered a condition known as *"The God Complex."* He actually thought he was God! Or Melchizedek! He never asked others for their opinion. He simply told everyone what he wanted and how he wanted it; and he assumed that everyone would cater to his every whim. Servicious lacked a lot in his character; one of his greatest character deficiencies being *common sense.*

SCHADEN

It is difficult to move away from describing the actions of Schaden because she is a piece of work. Before she had even been sworn in following the elections results, she announced that she would not be running again in two years. Her excuse was that she believed in "*term limits.*" Whom did she think she was fooling? The real reason was that she didn't have the money to run again because she was one of those righteous politicians who says they don't accept money from PACs. Hey! That's how the game was played. So either you were in the game or you were out. The self-righteous one who had knocked others for accepting campaign contributions from certain entities perhaps now saw the importance of having substantial donors. Those individuals that she had criticized would still be running, winning, and holding office while she would be back in the boonies thinking evil.

While Schaden may not have run for re-election, that did not stop her from scheming and attempting to pull strings in the background to destroy successful citizens. Her antics ranged from denigrating certain ethnic groups with bitter rants among her trusted friends to making attempts to close businesses of successful businessmen who were of a different political affiliation. And while she thought she was undermining in the dark, her every move was illuminating the community via snitches who were unbeknownst to her.

CLEOPATRA

Cleopatra had been contemplating moving to the eastern shore of the State of Xenolina because she was getting older and her beauty was fading. She didn't like the look of her pallid skin as it contrasted in stark measure to her long black hair. She felt the cold temperatures of High Ground where she lived was also contributing to the lines that were forming around her eyes and on her forehead. She felt that if she could get to the beach, there would be many days that she could work on getting tanned and perhaps some of the signs of aging wouldn't be so noticeable. This way her physical appearance would more closely resemble the character whose name she had borrowed.

It just so happened that the Kinder County Coterie was reaching out state-wide to find a candidate to conform to plans to shake up Kinder County Government—or at least certain departments within local government. Cleopatra fit the mold. She was cold, calculating, mean-spirited, and devious. She would be a perfect fit for the Coterie, as all those qualities gave a mirror-image description of the majority of Coterie members.

So Cleopatra was selected and brought to Kinder County with an agenda that she carried out with a vengeance. She did not hesitate to immediately begin her acts of treachery against targeted, unsuspecting employees. Her actions would eventually prove to be some of the biggest mistakes a Kinder County official had ever made.

FIREHORSE

One individual known as the old Firehorse, an elected official who was a highly educated professional, a skilled debater, and politically astute, gave Schaden a real scare during the campaign. While opposing Schaden for the seat she currently held, he still effectively managed the elected position that he held at that time. Firehorse was an entrepreneur, a retired General of the U.S. Military, a community activist, and a promoter of humanitarianism issues. In other words, Firehorse was a force to be reckoned with because he was revered by the citizens of Kinder County. He participated in community events, volunteering his professional expertise to ensure success of numerous Kinder County festivals. The old Firehorse gave Schaden a run for her money and caused her to spend money she didn't have. Hello, credit cards!

Here is a message for Schaden: Try spending some of the time you are going to have on hand "wondering" what might have been in store for you had you been less vicious, less mean, less controlling, less devious, less pretentious, a lesser chameleon, or a lesser witch.

All of the people Schaden targeted to drag through the mud and destroy are surviving just great. Whether Schaden knew it or not, Schaden, they knew who she was and what she was; they just didn't know why she was the way she was. Perhaps she didn't even know this herself. Don't dwell on the "Why." If they make it through the Pearly Gates, Firehorse intended to have a long conversation with Schaden to discuss how things might have been. It might have been better for the people of Kinder County if Firehorse had won the election and Schaden had lost. At least Firehores was an honorable man. But Schaden's integrity, by her own actions, had been grossly compromised.

SUNSHINE

A relatively heavy snow brought excitement to Kinder County. It came on January 10. While most citizens and neighbors were enjoying the snow, the Coterie was scheming against Sunshine, trying to conjure up a way to coerce him into resigning his position in order for the group to reduce or eliminate transparency, since they were constantly devising ways to keep the public and Kinder County employees in the dark. Like many citizens of Kinder Coun- ty, Sunshine was a member of a family with excellent work ethics. He grew up on a farm where his parents instilled sound moral and ethical values in him and his siblings. Sunshine was a delightful child. Anyone in his presence could see how happy he was because his parents, day in and day out, took every opportunity to provide a better life for their children. In his pre-teen and teen years, Sunshine had already blossomed into a leader. His leadership characteristics were obvious in his church and community. In school Sunshine was always an honor student who was very accommodating and outgoing, participating wholeheartedly and volunteering on the spot for whatever needed to be done. These fine qualities had followed Sunshine into adulthood, presenting somewhat of a problem for the Coterie.

Sunshine was the brightest star in the Coterie, yet other Coterie members tried to always keep Sunshine eclipsed. They cooked up schemes to do, or undo, issues that were for the county's good or detriment, and would not let Sunshine know what was being planned.

Sunshine was a true-believer in transparency, and he let his position be known by always keeping the public enlightened. However, wholesome ideas that would be good for the people of Kinder County, and good for people in general, presented to the Coterie by Sunshine were often shot down or dismissed as insignificant. When Sunshine once voiced his opinion about the many cases where divisive issues impeded the progression of good government in the 21st Century, he was openly criticized. He proposed the idea of creating a Community Relations Commission because he was being bombarded with complaints from

Kinder County employees who believed that they were receiving maltreatment and/or being discriminated against in the work force. And for offering the idea of creating a Community Relations Commission as a tool to deal with issues of this nature, Sunshine was verbally attacked for even broaching the idea of inclusiveness.

Sunshine was described as an "*activist*" Coterie member, and it was said that he wanted to begin *troubleshooting* the divisive issues that were continuously presented to him. What's wrong with that? Somebody needed to be brave enough to step forward and meet this challenge, rather than turning away from the problem. *And it was a problem*! Still is! Whereas some observers felt that Kinder County Coterie members recognized and respected the beliefs and practices of those who differed, it just wasn't so. Still isn't! And that is why Sunshine stepped out on a limb to try and bring about a much needed change. As a "*change agent*," Sunshine stated that what was good for one, should be good for all. He hoped that by establishing a Community Relations Commission, Kinder County Government would benefit by *enhanced communication, greater conflict resolution, more research and study of troublesome issues,* and *more public forums*.

Sunshine's idea was rejected as meaningless

because a direct focus was not stated at the outset, and specific problems weren't defined. But the problems were obvious although a large segment of Kinder County's population had put on blinders. And by doing so, discriminatory problems continued to persist. Redhawk's situation was a case in point. Had there been a Community Relations Commission operating in Kinder County, Servicious and the Coterie would not have been able to get by with the injustices they perpetrated on Redhawk and many other county employees. But as the saying goes, *"They might have gotten by, but they won't get away"*! A higher power reigns!

So it was necessary to get rid of Sunshine because he kept the public informed and would not   be persuaded to hide important issues from taxpay- ers, and/or sweep important matters under the rug. This plan to get rid of Sunshine would continue for months. And by September, the Coterie had nearly broken Sunshine's spirit. One of his colleagues was contemplating running for the office of Sheriff. This upset Sunshine because everyone knew that the Sheriff of Kinder County had a great love for the citizens, performed in an excellent fashion, held the highest moral and ethical standards, and had a sound value system. So what could this other guy improve upon in law enforcement? Sunshine was overwrought. Add to this idea the fact that Schaden had announced that she wanted to run to join the Kinder County Coterie again. They were all making it clear to Sunshine that, although he was an elected official same as they were, he was no longer welcome in the Coterie. Don't know what sort of pressure tactics they used on Sunshine, but somehow the Coterie managed to create a milieu of fear for Sunshine to the extent that Sunshine was visibly shaken, often expressing how threatening and menacing the Coterie was toward him. When it was suggested that Sunshine voice his concerns to the Kinder County Sheriff, Sunshine refused and said he could not. He did not give a reason. So then it was suggested to Sunshine that he contact the Xenolina Valuation Inquirer or X.V.I. The X.V.I. conducts inquiries and assessments that support counties when there appears to be situations, real or imagined, that local law enforcement needs assistance from agents who are more sophisticatedly trained to resolve impending or existing problems. But Sunshine was too fearful of retaliation, knowing that the Coterie would know it was he who had made the report against the Coterie. The Coterie was telling Sunshine to resign and take a state job. Although frightened he refused, of course, and remained on the Board for a while longer.

At one point during the crafty plan to drive

Sunshine out of Kinder County Government Sunshine was flogged by a supposedly good friend who felt that Sunshine had betrayed his trust during the election that had just taken place. It seems that the two friends, Sunshine and his colleague, were planning to build a new future for Kinder County, but the friend lost the election. While the friend was not bitter over having lost the election, he was highly upset because he felt that Sunshine had betrayed his trust. It is believed that the destruction of this friendship was the final straw for Sunshine, because shortly afterward, Sunshine caved under pressure and resigned from the Kinder County Coterie.

From the Coterie's vantage point, Sunshine also stood in the way of their efforts to rid Kinder County Government of Redhawk. Since they had not been able to convince Sunshine to leave sooner, they took another route to eliminate Redhawk. Schaden and Servicious ensnared the Waste Director into the web of treachery, giving her ultimate power to get rid of Redhawk *by any means necessary*! So three days after Sunshine left Kinder County Government, Redhawk was called into a conference and given a *written warning* for an imaginary personnel violation.

SCHADEN

Schaden was a member of the body that made laws for the Xenolina. So she devised a way to destroy, not only Redhawk, but the agency that Redhawk directed for then nearly 30 years. She presented a bill to merge the Waste Department with the Department of Alliance Activity.

It cannot be emphasized enough how deep- ly obsessed Schaden was with the idea of removing Redhawk from the position of DAA Director in Kinder County Government. One of her first desperate ploys to force Redhawk from the position was to convince her Coterie colleagues to vote to remove the DAA from the building in which the department was housed. As it was, there existed an old building that was no longer suitable for occupancy that once housed elderly and disabled citizens, but Schaden had convinced the

51

County Keeper at that time to purchase the building for the purpose of storing Kinder County equipment and supplies. It seemed like a good idea to the unsuspecting onlooker if the building were really being purchased for that purpose. But being the devious, undermining individual that she is, Schaden had another purpose in mind. She believed that if Redhawk and the DAA were cast into that old, sick building, Redhawk would be angry enough to quit the job she loved and performed so well.

Schaden was mistaken. Even though years earlier Redhawk had campaigned throughout Kinder County in the 1980s with the more intelligent Coterie members requesting a building with suitable office space for serving needy citizens, being thrown from the new building was not the end of the world—nor would it be the end or Redhawk's career.

So Redhawk and the DAA staff moved into the mold-infested, mildew-infested, critter-infested, termite-infested, half-renovated building in the year 2001. There were several points Redhawk was glad about when this happened. The most important being that her mother, who had passed in the year 2000, was not alive to witness this maltreatment. Another fact that made Redhawk happy was that Schaden, in all her treachery, was not going to have her way, one more time.

Schaden bragged to members of the Coterie and community about how she had thrown Redhawk from a new building into the dump of a building across the street. She was quoted as saying, "Yes, I did it dammit, and I would do it again!" And then she laughed that roughish laugh for which she is so famous.

While the old building was undergoing its shoddy renovation, Schaden had her friends who lived it the town of Marigold, where the DAA Department is located, walk their dogs on that street. They were instructed to walk their dogs to the front of the building and have the dogs urinate at the front door. Having been conditioned this way, the dogs continued this behavior on a daily basis after the renovations had been completed. So when Redhawk and staff finally moved into the building, every morning when they went through the front door, the scent of animal urine greeted them on a daily basis. Clients even complained about the stench and wondered what was causing the raunchy smell. Although Redhawk knew its origin, because a derelict who hung around the building at night had told her what was causing the stench, she never revealed that tidbit to anyone. It was a fact too provocative to voice. Yet it was typical Schaden style.

MAYOR PETER GUNN

The town of Marigold deserves greater mention, because the appearance of this quaint little town belies how far the town has truly advanced from the days of yesteryear. The most significant indication of progress is the fact that Peter Gunn, the Mayor, and members of the Town Council appointed a Police Chief that did not, according to the people's expectations, fit what the people considered the norm.

Now Mayor Peter Gunn was not your typical dull, average run-of-the-mill type of a Mayor. He was quite colorful, and a delightful engaging person who always sought the best in anybody he happened to meet. He would converse with the man on the street as readily as he would another public official about conditions of the town and his plans for making improvements. The Mayor could be described as a "*par-*

ticipatory" Mayor. If there were a church or religious declaration needing a *"Proclamation"* for the event, Mayor Peter Gunn was available to share his enthusiasm for whatever the situation demanded. He could be seen at community barbeques adorned with an apron and serving up a dish. If situations or events were somber, Mayor Peter Gunn was there. If situations or events happened to be celebratory, the Mayor could be seen illuminating the crowd with his hearty laugh and jovial personality.

Some of his ideas did not set well with the old guard who wanted Marigold to step back into the 19th century, and this created a rift between the Mayor and some of his longtime supporters.

CHIEF MONTANA SOUTHERLAND

Mayor Peter Gunn and the Town Council appointed a female Police Chief—a first. Now, while on the one hand this was commendable, at the same time it was most appropriate because she was the most qualified applicant at the time, this appointment was totally unexpected.

Her name was Montana Southerland, and she hailed from the northern section of Kinder County. To some onlookers, her beauty might have camou- flaged her toughness. But any time a situation pre- sented itself in which her law enforcement skill was required, she met the challenge with tremendous verve. Montana was married to Dawson Southerland, a poetic man who also worked in law enforcement as an officer for the Xenolina Department of Correc- tions. Montana and Dawson were the proud parents of two handsome successful sons.

As time went by with Montana serving as Chief of Police of the Town of Marigold, one of the old guard, a long-standing attorney in town, decided that there were too many women holding what he considered powerful positions in the Town of Marigold and Kinder County overall, and he set out to take conditions back to a time before progress brought diversity to the area. As far as he was concerned, a woman's place was to remain subservient, and the public positions of prestige belonged to men. So he put a plan in motion against Montana.

The first step was to begin severe criticism of every decision Chief Montana Southerland made, even though the decisions were right and governed by laws and general statutes. That didn't really curtail the attorney and his cohorts because they ruled with an iron fist, and anyone who questioned them or attempted to intervene or interfere in any way became mincemeat. So one of those times after an unwarranted reprimand had been thrust upon Chief Montana, she was suspended with pay for a period of 11 days. When she returned to work at the end of the suspension, the climate at police headquarters had reached the sub-zero zone. For the next several days at work the Chief was shunned, as no one would communicate with her. Deciding that it would be impossible to lead in such a cold, callous atmosphere, Chief Montana Southerland resigned the position of Chief of Police of the Town of Marigold.

While Chief Montana's resignation went to the hearts of many Marigold citizens, the new Mayor and Town Council soon appointed a new Police Chief. Jay Host, the replacement Police Chief, was a great choice. Host was recruited from the Kinder County Sheriff Department with an extensive background in law enforcement, and was a man of great integrity. With his appointment, the Town of Marigold would soon begin again to reflect 21st century visions for diversification and actualization that Chief Montana had begun to implement prior to being trammeled by Marigold's powerbroker.

So, anyone can guess what eventually happened at one of the future elections in the Town of Marigold. Yes, Peter Gunn was defeated. The magnitude of this loss will be felt well into the future of the Town of Marigold.

MARIGOLD COURTHOUSE

In this quaint little town, as in many southern towns, stands the courthouse as its most central feature. Once you have rounded the courthouse square, there are some sights that stand out as tourist attractions. A lot of the town's character surrounds its courthouse. There are some old stores, reminiscent of the 1940s and 1950s that are appealing to anyone who relished that era. Nearby, a restaurant serves as a reminder that many local neighbors came from Mexico or Puerto Rico. The red-tile roof on the stucco structure offers a picturesque scene straight out of Guadalajara or San Juan.

On any given day, a diverse group of citizens can be observed engaging in snippets of local gossip as well as discussing issues of importance for Kind- er County. On another side of the courthouse an old

Presbyterian church beckons all who will to come worship with the townspeople. Majestic old homes stand interspersed among more modern structures, establishing Marigold as a symbol of welcome to the young and the old.

And then there is the old jail that has been renovated and used for office space downstairs. Upstairs, the original cells serve as a reminder of days gone by when many of Kinder County fathers slept there, if for nothing more than to sleep off a hangover after having taken two aspirins so that they could go home and face the wrath of the wife in the morning.

And today is no different in the modern new jail that's located in close proximity to the old jail, except where men years ago were locked up for moonshining, today the vice of choice seems to be some form of more menacing drugs—cocaine, methamphetamines, marijuana, and the like. But just as it was in times past, the Sheriff and his deputies work diligently to keep Kinder County as free as possible of those sorts of things. It is not an enviable task, and great effort is put forth toward this cleanup on an ongoing basis. Which means, of course, that the new jail, which has now become the old jail, being as small as it is, can't properly or adequately house the number of inmates that tends to keep mushrooming. One of these days the Kinder County Coterie is going to realize the inevitability of having to build a newer, state-of-the-art facility to accommodate the growing needs of Kinder County. Since it is known that Kinder County is rapidly increasing its population, it stands to reason that facility needs are also increasing.

Between the courthouse and the jail, there are many sad stories to be told. There have been many truths, lies, and innuendoes floated about in the Kinder County courthouse. There have been justices and, in some instances, injustices served upon both law-abiding citizens and law-breaking citizens. Good mothers have seen the sons they raised to be good sons taken away from them for years because the lessons taught were not the code of conduct those sons chose to live by.

Many babies have sat, unknowingly, listening to their biological fathers deny paternity, while their fathers go so far as to brand the mothers as "*loose women*" rather than someone they chose to love during perhaps what was a one-night-stand. Thus, many babies that have sat through those depositions have carried the title of "*love child.*" Is there any wonder that years hence those babies will probably return to the courtroom as adults who have followed in their daddies' footsteps?

On the other hand, some of the babies previously mentioned have grown up to become officers of the court, attorneys, good citizens serving as jurors and grand jurors, and through their life experiences have been able to contribute to justice being served in a fair and impartial manner.

That same stately courthouse has witnessed people being secretly accused, with the accusa- tions heard only by Grand Juries that use wisdom and common sense to decipher facts and determine whether or not an individual should be tried for committing the crime that has been suggested, often by their so-called friends or known enemies, or accusers who appear to be jealous demons bent on destroying someone else's happiness because they themselves are miserable, leading miserable lives without hope of ever crawling out of the barrel in which they have found themselves.

This surely was the case when Schaden, Servicious, and Cleopatra, along with a few others, conspired, insinuated, and declared that Redhawk had committed some fraudulent acts while serving her tenure as DAA Director. They searched records, listened to lying citizens, and a certain DAA staff member and others, but only found that they had wasted their time following a multiplex of lies born out of envy, jealousy, incompetency, and plain old hatred. In the final analysis, they could not take away the   benefits for which Redhawk had worked so hard throughout her lifetime—not her social security, nor retirement benefits, nor her 104-Z. But they tried! Imagine that!

REDHAWK

Redhawk spent her last five years as DAA Director constructively working in the midst of adversity. At the beginning of her career, her appointment and subsequent work as a servant leader had been a wonderfully gratifying experience. The individuals who had appointed her to the position and the Coterie that had confirmed her appointment were more than just the average, good southern Christians. They were intelligent human beings who recognized that they were making a bold decision in the best inter- est of Kinder County for the betterment of public ser- vice for the people of Kinder County. Moreover, and above all, they were brave souls. Because in a county where desegragation had been slowly manifesting it- self, they had boldly stepped forward and appointed the first double minority County Director of Alliance

Activity in the State of Xenolina to lead a DAA agency as executive director. This was in the early 1980s. As a matter of fact, the appointment was confirmed during the Coterie's meeting on Dec. 22, 1982.

Redhawk's first day on the new job was Jan. 4, 1983. What an experience! The appointment had to be, without a doubt, an appointment from God. And through all the days of Redhawk's career, she promised to do God's work. Keeping this promise in the forefront daily, she knew the disadvantaged, low-income citizens of Kinder County who needed to utilize the services offered at the Department of Alliance Activity would be better served. And this is the theme she set forth for all staff who worked under her leadership. She often could be heard saying, "We are doing God's work!" No matter who looks upon us with criticism, belittling the clients we serve, God is watching and He is pleased with what we do and the way we are doing it—with compassion. For we not only serve well within the bounds of rules, guidelines, and laws governing our work, we go above and beyond the call of duty to bring comfort to families, to feed the hungry, and to especially save children and the elderly from abuse and neglect.

The Kinder County Department of Alliance Activity, thanks to one of many of Redhawk's initiatives, had its own small food pantry. The general public would have been surprised at the number of people who went to DAA without a morsel of food and no means of obtaining food until their Food Stamp benefits were received. The DAA pantry allowed DAA staff to give needy families boxes of food containing various canned meats, vegetables, pasta, rice, soups, cereal, canned fruits, etc. For someone who was hungry and had not had a meal in many days, those donations of food were a godsend. The food that stocked the pantry had been purchased by Redhawk and the DAA staff, donated by Boy Scouts completing special projects, and by schools and community groups and individuals and members of the Board of Alliance Activity who understood the needs of Kinder County's less fortunate citizens.

The Board of Alliance Activity and Redhawk established agreements with grocery chain stores that allowed the Department of Alliance Activity to collect food whose expirations dates were near that could be given to needy citizens rather than have the food thrown away because it could no longer be sold. Families and individuals were served in a proud and respectful manner and those families expressed much gratitude for the caring nature of DAA staff. At the time, this gesture was unique to Kinder County.   It spoke of the depth of concern and level of dedication Kinder County DAA offered its needy citizens. This was just one example of the agency's resourcefulness in public service.

But during the last few years Redhawk was employed in Kinder County Government, the Coterie operated to ensure that adversity was the norm in their effort to frustrate Redhawk out of the job she so skillfully and professionally performed daily. Cleopatra even axed the DAA food pantry and gave all the food from the pantry to another agency, another example of how little Cleopatra cared about the well-being of DAA clients.

The journey was long and hard; the roads were rough and tough, but Redhawk met and faced their many challenges and got through all the potholes and trenches unscathed. Bruised and battered, but unscathed. They wanted to put her life in shambles. Their harassment and aggravating tactics would intensify with Cleopatra at the helm, every time some of their unwarranted negative actions were questioned. Redhawk had the uncanny ability to turn personal pain and disappointment in the people who so cruelly perpetrated an injustice against her into therapeutic action by writing an account of who and what they are, and how they operate to advance their greed and quest for power in the name of governing. In their quest for ultimate control, they knowingly break rules against others in order to get what they want—including violating federal law when they want to be rid of an employee. The pressure to keep quiet and ignore the maltreatment is highly distressing for anyone forced to swallow their outrage of the cruel treatment perpetrated by Servicious and the Coterie. It is difficult to speak out against institutional discrimination because onlookers have been duped into believing that the so-called *"powers-that-be"* in Kinder County Government are fair and impartial. That notion is the joke of the century!

But *"anger"* is not a plan for resolving issues. We must understand people and get over our anger and move into a sphere that is good for our souls. Recriminations should be abandoned. All one needs to do is simply speak the truth. And speaking of the 104-Z Fund, over the years Redhawk had a small savings that she had contributed to throughout her years in the work force. Unbelievably, during the "Investigatory Leave Fiasco," which will be addressed later, they even tried to take that away. When Redhawk tried to rollover the 104-Z funds to the Super Power (State of Xenolina) that would be paying her monthly retirement benefits, darned if the creeps didn't try to take the money she had saved. It took four whole months before the funds were finally rolled into Redhawk's state account so she could begin receiving the benefits monthly. The Coterie was lowdown beyond belief. If anyone had before this time told Redhawk that they were that lowdown and dirty, she would not have believed it. But, as they say, "seeing is believing"! Yes, it happened, and until this day, and for the rest of her days on Earth, Redhawk will never be able to reckon how people who pretend to be so upstanding and high and mighty can be so lowdown and dirty.

Redhawk, a respectable individual, was put through extreme emotional distress, betrayed and besmirched by her alleged superiors. They tried to steal her peace and stability. It is difficult to imagine that Cleopatra and her handlers had that much personal hatred for one individual. Redhawk could never have imagined the gravity of their treachery. They made judgments based upon their warped imaginations, and false or fabricated evidence, and malicious gossip.

These are the people having access to all of Redhawk's confidential background information—social security number, date of birth, etc. They used this to probe into Redhawk's bank accounts, all the while getting more desperate with each stone they unturned because they did not find anything to substantiate the lies they had been told, nor the sick ideas they, themselves, had conjured up in their own cracked heads. With each new discovery of how meticulously Redhawk had prepared for her future, the envy mushroomed to something synonymous to an emotional nuclear explosion.

And revenge is hell! Vengeance is mine saith the Lord, but it is also known that God expects us to take good care of our own minds and bodies, which can be interpreted to mean that we must do things and take the actions that are pleasing to Him while on this Earth. So when we have been seriously harmed, it is best to seriously retaliate in a manner that is truthful and justifiable. The pen is mightier than the sword. So if it is therapeutic to write about misfortunate incidents that have occurred in life, and by all means do so with gusto and, as in Redhawk's case, let the readers—the general public—decide if this was the right road to travel. Remember to do unto others as you would have them do unto you. That's the Gold- en Rule! To tell the truth, the whole truth in a way that reveals events in question. The truth is what sets us free and it must be told if we are to live peacefully and harmoniously in Kinder County.

Redhawk believed that someone had to stand up to the Coterie, and felt that at the time, it had to be her because heretofore no one had ever stood up to them. So she put on her Armor of God and stepped onto the battlefield against the Kinder County Coterie and the henchwoman hired to destroy her. Redhawk felt comfortable about the path she was taking to cope with the disorder the Coterie and Cleopatra had created in her life.

CLEOPATRA

Now Cleopatra, the Waste Director, was a relatively new player in the Kinder County Coterie. She was loved by Servicious, so that gave her *carte blanche* in Kinder County Government to do whatever she wanted to, whenever she wanted to. Cleopatra was a big spender and an even greater manipulator. She hailed from a region of Xenolina known as High Ground, where poverty was prevalent and she was not accustomed to having her needs met easily. So when she was given a blank check in Kinder Coun- ty, she began to spend foolishly and elaborately. She refurbished the Waste Department from floor to ceiling---putting in new, expensive tile floors on top of floors that were not even damaged; threw away perfectly good furniture and replaced it with all new furniture that was more to her liking; and replaced perfectly good cabinets and counters in all the examining rooms, essentially wasting nearly a million dollars on objects that were not needed.

If that weren't enough, she began purchas- ing uniform shirts as if her life depended on Waste Department staff having a montage of various colored uniform shirts. In fact, Waste Department staff sported different colors of shirts for different days of the week. Staff began to joke about Cleopatra's effort to build a *rainbow coalition* of shirts and questioned Cleopatra's motive for this senseless waste. As it turned out, the owners of the company that produced the shirts just happened to have been Cleopatra's good friends. So Cleopatra was impressing her friends and keeping them in business while she herself had created another kickback scheme using Kinder County revenue. All of this waste was ignored by the Coterie. As a matter of fact, members of the Coterie were constantly praising Cleopatra for her great waste.

For reasons unknown, it appeared that Cleopatra filled a dual role as the chairman of the Coterie and County Keeper in addition to her role as Waste Director. Her friend Ray Rivers from High Ground had the actual title of County Keeper but was fearful of Servicious. Cleopatra was not afraid of Servicious because she as good as had Servicious in bed. She had every opportunity to rendezvous with Servicious handed to her because her own husband, a saint blinded by love, was always on the go performing humanitarian deeds for the less fortunate, both in and out of the country. And you know what they say—while the cat's away, the mice will play. And although it was unseen by some, rumor had it, from many sources, that Cleopatra and Servicious had a thing going on.

ZIGGY BLUE

One of Servicious' other girlfriends, Ziggy Blue, was one of the people spreading the story about Cleopatra and Servicious, because she was feeling like a woman scorned. What a joke! She wasn't Servicious' wife. Ziggy, herself, was a piece of work. She had orchestrated the demise of the previous Waste Director in hopes of gaining the position for herself. Many of her co-workers and colleagues were perplexed by Ziggy's behavior because it was her boss, Dr. Josh Gomes, Medical Department Director before the Medical Department was converted to a Waste Department, who was largely responsible for her having successfully completed her college degree. Dr. Gomes had written papers for Ziggy, completed many other assignments for her and allowed her a flexible schedule so that she could have study time and attend classes while gainfully employed at the Medical Department.

Ziggy was not the first person to use another human being to advance their special interests and then turn against their mentor once their momentary personal mission had been accomplished. While Dr. Gomes might have been floored by Ziggy's behavior, he should have seen it coming. But being the good guy that he is, he was unsuspecting, and thus became victim of the ultimate *coup d'état.*

PART II

JOSH GOMES

Ziggy was a prissy, cunning woman who used her girlish wiles to entangle unsuspecting souls in a web of deceit. She hooked up with Servicious to destroy Josh Gomes, the Medical Director. Dr. Gomes managed the Medical Department before it became a Waste Department. Prior to Cleopatra's entry on the scene, Ziggy Blue had thought the relationship between her and Servicious would last forever and that Servicious would appoint her Director of the Medical Department. However, when Cleopatra, the new director was hired, she converted the Medical Department to the Waste Department, and Servicious dropped Ziggy like a hot potato. Ziggy had orchestrated the demise of her boss, Dr. Gomes, but nothing was gained for Ziggy.

In the spring a few years earlier, during Kinder

County's budget preparation period, the Kinder County Keeper, Rock Boston, had approached Dr. Gomes' Executive Accountant, Genevieve Scott, offering that Kinder County was facing a budget shortfall. He then stated that each department would be expected to reduce budgets to reflect the Coterie's budget requirements. He suggested that the Medical Department could reduce its budget by cutting four to six personnel, and proceeded to present a list of names to consider for reduction in force. (*The County Keeper later denied that the conversation had taken place, but Genevieve Scott had in her possession the list of names that Rock Boston had given her*). One name on the list was the Hispanic clerk Francesca Santiago, who worked with clinical clerical staff. Her language skills were in demand because many patients visiting the Medical Department were Hispanic and did not speak English. So, there was a growing need for Spanish translating skills in all departments of Kinder County Government, most especially at the Medical Department and the Department of Alliance Activity.

Because she did not understand the dynamics of what was taking place, Francesca Santiago began to complain publicly through an anonymous letter that implied she was the target of racial discrimina- tion. Following the first anonymous letter, a series of anonymous letters, along with some letters that had been signed by nurses working under the supervision of Ziggy Blue that had been penned by Ziggy Blue herself. While the nurses were afraid to tell that Ziggy had written the letters and instructed them to sign their names, a search of Ziggy Blue's county-owned computer hard-drive revealed every letter the nurses had signed had been written on Ziggy Blue's coun- ty-owned computer. One nurse who was loyal to Dr. Gomes admitted that Ziggy Blue herself had written the letter the nurse had signed. The nurse stated that Ziggy Blue had told her that if she did not sign the letter, Ziggy Blue was going to fire her when Ziggy Blue became Medical Department Director. Dr. Gomes' Executive Assistant, Dee Moore, witnessed the conversation. Later, under duress, the nurse denied having admitted that Ziggy Blue had written the letter.

When that scheme did not generate the results Servicious had expected and hoped for, he sent the County Keeper, accompanied by the County Analyst, back to the Medical Department, this time to visit Dr. Gomes. During this visit Etum Sword, the County Analyst, suggested that the best method for resolving the problems that were brewing at the Medical Department would be for Dr. Gomes to rid himself and the Medical Department of Genevieve Scott and his troubles would "*disappear.*" Of course, both the Keeper and the Analyst later denied that they had suggested that Dr. Gomes should terminate the employment of Genevieve Scott. But Dr. Gomes' statements were corroborated by his Executive Assistant, Dee Moore, who overheard the conversation. Dr. Gomes believed that this abhorrent action was an attempt to use Genevieve Scott as a scapegoat in order to cover up political corruption of the Coterie. All of this was happening only a few months short of Genevieve Scott's 30-year retirement. This action by the Coterie and County Keeper, had it been successful, would have deprived Genevieve Scott of retirement benefits offered by Kinder County. Genevieve Scott had served under Dr. Gomes throughout his 14-year tenure as Kinder County Medical Department Director and had shown him great loyalty and considerable administrative acumen. Dr. Gomes was not going to be a party to such an act against her.

As Dr. Gomes and Genevieve continued the budget preparation process following Rock Boston's last visit, Dr. Gomes decided he had little choice but to terminate Francesca Santiago's employment as Rock Boston had first suggested because she was already working beyond the term of her employment contract. As expected, Miss Santiago was distraught over the decision.

Almost immediately, the number of unsigned letters complaining about the Medical Department's management and racial discrimination of Hispanics escalated and became a daily occurrence. Letters were sent to the Medical Department Board and the Coterie. The letters were never shared with Dr. Gomes, but he was informed of their existence. During a Medical Department Board meeting, one member who had been recently appointed to the Medical Board complained about the number of letters he had received. He waved the letters in the air during the meeting, but he never shared copies of the letters with Dr. Gomes. Later on, letters that had been signed by employees under Ziggy Blue's supervision were published in the media. Following the chaos Dr. Gomes transferred Ziggy Blue to the outpost Kinder County Government Annex. Again, the letters that were published in the media were found on the hard drive of Ziggy Blue's county-owned computer.

COUP ATTEMPT

To fully understand the magnitude of Ziggy Blue's treachery requires turning back the clock a few years. Dr. Gomes had hired Ziggy Blue several years before she became engaged in her desperate attempt to overthrow him so that she could be appointed Director of the Kinder County Medical Department. In the beginning, Dr. Gomes had observed that Ziggy Blue appeared to be performing her duties quite well. Over a period of years, he promoted Ziggy through the organizational hierarchy until she became Supervisor of Medical Nurses in the Medical Department's clinics.

At some point Ziggy began to feel powerful and she mustered the nerve to tell Dr. Gomes that she wanted his job! She said, "I want to be Medical Department Director!" At the time, she made the statement, Ziggy didn't even have a college degree. Being the humble, patient man that he was, Dr. Gomes told Ziggy that she would need a four-year degree and a master's degree, probably in the medical field or in administration in order to qualify for the job. He then gave Ziggy his wholehearted support in her effort to earn a Bachelor of Science in Nursing and Master's Degree in Administration. Ziggy enrolled in an online program through Phoenix University.

Ziggy Blue became extremely arrogant once she enrolled in Phoenix University. She began to ask Dr. Gomes when was he going to retire. Dr. Gomes told Ziggy that he would retire when he was ready, and he said perhaps he would be ready in five years. Ziggy did not like Dr. Gomes' reply to her question and it showed all over her face. Dr. Gomes told her, once again, that he was not ready to retire.

Shortly after Ziggy Blue hinted to Dr. Gomes that she was ready for him to retire, he began to hear from various sources that Ziggy Blue was telling Medical Department staff that she was going to be the new Medical Department Director. However, at that time Dr. Gomes had been concerned that the number of patients being treated in the Public Medical Clinics was lower than had been anticipated. To substantiate this notion, he began to review patient *"sign in"* sheets daily and weekly. It soon became clear to Dr.

Gomes that the contract physician who visited the Public Medical Clinics three times weekly was being seriously under-utilized. Staff began to inform Dr. Gomes that patients—primarily Hispanic patients who needed to be seen by a physician—were being sent to Kinder Memorial Hospital for care. Ziggy, of course, denied that the patient transfer was occurring, and stated that she would ensure that the Medical Department's contract physician always had patients to care for on the days he was available at the clin- ics. Unfortunately, Ziggy Blue continued her scheme of channeling Hispanic patients to Kinder Memorial Hospital so the situation at the Public Medical Clinic failed to improve.

Dr. Gomes began putting forth monumental efforts to improve patient treatment for citizens visiting the Public Medical Clinics. Concurrently, he was also attempting to organize the establishment of two new primary medical care programs in Pediatrics and Internal Medicine. He was on his way to building a two-tier system whereby medical care could be provided for indigents and low-income citizens with the most qualified medical specialists available. He was able to secure contracts with two exceptionally qualified physicians in the field of Pediatrics and Internal Medicine. These physicians were to use the Medical Department's facilities, hire their own support   staff, manage their own medical clinics, and provide the best available medical care for the citizens of Kind- er County. This plan almost came to fruition, except Ziggy Blue used her special relationship and connection with Servicious to intentionally sabotage these medical care programs.

During the period of his several years on the Board of the Medical Department, Servicious had fought against every innovative medical care initiative and program Dr. Gomes instituted, or attempted to implement. This included the development of the primary dental clinic; the mobile dental clinic; and the establishment of Board Certified Physicians within the Kinder County Medical Department to provide primary health care services to low-income and indigent patients. Servicious was infamously quoted in the local news media as saying, *"People didn't need to see a doctor."* He believed that having a *"Physi- cian's Assistant"* was all the people of Kinder County needed for good health care. Dr. Gomes disagreed because he knew that even though there is a place in the profession for well-trained Physician Assistants and Nurse Practitioners in patient care, the missing element those two entities did not have was the diagnostic skills that are absolutely necessary in the practice of excellent medical care. These skills are taught to medical students in years three, four and post-doctoral training, but not necessarily in the licensure of PAs and NPs. However, Servicious, being uneducated in these matters, did not understand the dynamics necessary for ensuring that the medical care provided would be of the highest quality only if the appropriately trained professionals were in place to guarantee this.

Additionally, during the time Dr. Gomes was recruiting and employing the dentists and physicians needed to practice in the clinics, he had to oversee the remodeling of the Medical Department space that would be used by the dental and medical care clinics, and the design and development of the new mobile dental clinic. Within a short period of time, he had completed the remodeling, those clinics were providing services, and the medical specialists were treating patients. It was extremely important during this time to have the cooperation of the Clinic Nursing Supervisor, Ziggy Blue, with the physicians in the medical practices when laboratory and immunization services were requested. However, this did not happen without conflict among Ziggy Blue, the clinic nurse staff, and the medical providers in pediatrics and internal medicine.

Dr. Gomes discussed with Ziggy Blue his concerns about patients needing care at the Kinder County Medical Department, but were being diverted to

Kinder Memorial Hospital Emergency Department. And again Ziggy Blue assured him that she was not sending patients to the hospital for care rather than scheduling visits for them with the visiting physician in the Medical Department's public clinics or to the Medical Department's contract supported physicians. Ziggy Blue continued to lie to Dr. Gomes on this issue because she continued to regularly refer patients for treatment at Kinder Memorial Hospital Emergency Department.

During this interim period, Ziggy Blue posted a negative comment on Facebook about one of the doctors at the Kinder County Medical Department. Ziggy stated in her Facebook post that she would never take her child to that physician. Ziggy was called into Dr. Gomes' office where she apologized to Dr. Gomes and stated she was sorry for posting the comment on Facebook. (*Servicious put on blinders when his special friends committed unacceptable personal conduct and offenses, or exhibited behaviors that warranted written warning, but he never missed an opportunity to throw other employees under the bus*). In this particular instance, Dr. Gomes told Ziggy Blue, in no uncertain terms, that he would not support her or anyone for Kinder County Medical Department Director who exhibited such unprofessional behavior and who did not fully support the medical and dental clinics he had implemented. Ziggy said what needed to be said at that moment and assured Dr. Gomes that she would support his programs.

Sadly, Dr. Gomes discovered much later that Ziggy Blue was actively working to create con- flict between the nursing staff she supervised and the nurses working for the private physicians. Dr. Gomes believed Ziggy Blue conspired with the con- sulting nurse from the Xenolina State Department of Medicine. Nurses working in the medical clinics were not Kinder County Medical Department nurs- es. Those nurses supporting the physicians had been hired by the physicians as Physician's Practice Nurs- es. They were never trained as Public Medical Department Nurses and were not hired to fulfill those duties. Ziggy Blue had never voiced any concern to Dr. Gomes about this arrangement. What Ziggy Blue and her co-conspirator from the State of Xenolina wanted was *CONTROL* over all the nurses working at the Kinder County Medical Department. This placed the physician's nurses at loggerheads with Ziggy Blue and the Medical Department nurses. The physicians and their nurses had different clinic hours than the Kinder County Medical Department nurses, creating resentment among the Medical Department nurses. Ziggy Blue used her position, supported by the Xenolina Medical Department consulting nurse, to create unrest among the nurses in both the public Medical Department and private medical care clinics. Dr. Gomes requested a replacement consultant nurse since the one the State of Xenolina had sent to Kinder County had joined forces with Ziggy. However, by the time the consultant had been replaced, Ziggy Blue and her boyfriend, Servicious, had already created serious problems within the Kinder County Medical Department.

Only a few days following Dr. Gomes' conversation with Ziggy Blue concerning the pediatrician and support for the medical programs at Kinder County Medical Department, three Medical Department employees appeared on TV in pitiful disguise to complain about Kinder County Medical Department management. Ziggy Blue was easily recognizable and she was the only one to speak during the interview.

During the televised interview Ziggy lied and said (1) there was extensive drug use among staff and providers at the Kinder County Medical Department; (2) management refused to adequately train providers; (3) management committed fraud; and (4) there were racial discriminatory practices in management.

Ziggy Blue stated that illegal drug use was "*common*" among clinic staff. Not true! Ziggy could not produce names of any staff who used illegal, non-prescription drugs. In an apparent effort to have something to support her contention, Ziggy said that some time several years in the past she had smelled alcohol on the breath of a clerk, but she could not recall the clerk's name. Ziggy could not name a single staff member who was, or had been, using illegal drugs.

In terms of training, or the lack of it, as purported by Ziggy Blue, her charge that nurses at the Kinder County Medical Department were not providing the best care due to a lack of training was another lie! Records and documents confirmed that over the years, Dr. Gomes had sent a number of nurses to advanced nurse's training. Those nurses' credentials were easily verified. As a matter of fact, at the time Ziggy Blue made her TV complaint, one nurse under Ziggy's supervision had just returned from an extensive training program. Dr. Gomes, during his tenure as Medical Department Director, had sent two Public Medical Nurses to advanced training to become Nurse Practitioners (the highest level of training a nurse can achieve). In fact, Dr. Gomes had even let Ziggy Blue represent him at many management opportunities to help qualify her for the Director's position.

Regarding *"fraud,"* Ziggy Blue complained during the TV interview as well as in other interviews with the media that Kinder County Medical Department Administration was openly committing fraud. Servicious hung on to Ziggy's words as if they were the Gospel. So, he demanded an independent investigation of management in the Medical Department. Sunshine, who at the time was Coterie Chairman, wrote a public letter to the District Attorney asking for a *"criminal investigation"* of the Kinder County Medical Department. There was absolutely no fraud! The Xenolina State guidelines govern State of Xenolina, and although the term *"fraud"* was used by the Coterie members, Servicious, and Sunshine, as an excuse to request a criminal investigation of Kind- er County's Medical Department management, both Ziggy Blue and the Coterie soon *'revised'* their fraud allegations when they were confronted with the facts: *The Kinder County Medical Department staff had no connection with any actual dollars (except a small "petty cash" amount of less than $100 maintained by the Executive Accountant to handle small purchases or payment for supplies). All cash receipts were sent to the County Keeper's office at the end of each business day.* Like the other issues, the fraud issue was simply a bald-faced lie!

Dr. Gomes personally contacted the Kinder County Analyst, Etum Sword, and asked him to review any funding sources in the Medical Department and the handling of any monies to ascertain any possibility that fraud could possibly be occurring. The County Analyst assured Dr. Gomes that he understood the handling of money at the Medical Department and that fraud simply did not exist and was not an issue deserving an investigation. After all the hullabaloo, the fraud charge simply disappeared.

As for *"discriminatory racial practices"* in Medical Department management, the suggestion was utterly ridiculous! For a period of approximately three years, the Kinder County Medical Department provided the highest level of medical care to citizens in every demographic and racial group without any thought of the patient's race. Providers certified in Internal Medicine and Pediatrics treated any patient walking through the doors of the Medical Department needing medical care, without considering race or income. In fact, Kinder County Medical Department had the only pediatrician on the West side of the county that provided highly skilled diagnostic medical care services to low-income children in Kinder County. And the department's Mobile Dental Clin- ic provided dental care to low-income and indigent families by highly skilled dentist for the first time in their lives. Servicious fought against the establishment of the Mobile Clinic; the Primary Dental Clinic; the Pediatric Child Care Program; and the Internal Medicine Adult Health Care Program in every budget that Dr. Gomes presented to the Coterie! Servicious' idea of medical care for Kinder County's low-income and indigent population was juxtaposed with the very late Queen of France, Marie Antoinette, but instead of shouting, *"Let them eat cake!"* he said, *"Let them use a Physician Assistant. They're good enough for the common people!"*

Shortly before Ziggy Blue's TV interview had been aired, Servicious had met with Dr. Gomes, a member of Dr. Gomes' staff, and two of Servicious' constituents in the conference room of the Orchestration Building. Servicious introduced the two Kinder County residents and stated that they were *very unhappy* with the Medical Department and the staff in particular, because the staff would not issue a septic permit for a property the constituents wished to sell. During the entire meeting the two constituents had very little to say because Servicious was ranting in his usual intimidating fashion.

The staff, in a very professional manner, stated that they were sorry the property did not meet the State of Xenolina's mandated requirements for sewage permits. Servicious was outraged and behaved like a tyrant in reaction to the staff's statement. In an attempt to calm Servicious down, Dr. Gomes told Servicious that he would ask the Xenolina State District Sanitarian to conduct an evaluation of the property, and if he found the property to be acceptable, a permit would be issued. Servicious was not happy with the delay that would be necessary due to the time it would take to have a State Representative visit the property to conduct an assessment and make a determination. The atmosphere in the meeting grew progressively more tense.

When Servicious' constituents left the meeting, Dr. Gomes spoke with Servicious and told him that he (Dr. Gomes) did not believe that it was acceptable for any member of the Coterie to insert himself into the permitting process in an attempt to change the decision made by a highly trained, experienced staff in order for the applicants to be favored and get their wish, knowing the decision was against the State of Xenolina laws. *If looks could kill, Dr. Gomes would have been dead on the spot!*

Shortly after that meeting, Servicious held his first *press conference* to condemn the Kinder County Medical Department's management and demanded that an *"outside"* assessment of the Medical Department be conducted immediately. Servicious would have three investigations conducted of the Medical Department before he would stop the madness.

The first of three county-funded investigations was conducted by a former Medical Director from   a neighboring town. As reported by the local media, he was hired at the request of the Kinder County Keeper to provide an independent and unbiased assessment of the department. The County Keeper stated that recently a group of employees had reported unfair treatment, racial comments by staff, employee drug use, and HIPAA violations.

In conducting the so-called unbiased assessment, the investigator only interviewed 20 of the Kinder County Medical Department's staff of 70 members (28.5 percent); only interviewed staff that had been selected by the County Keeper; and did not interview a representative or statistically selected sample. He was critical of a common management organizations where personnel cross-training enables staff to perform more diverse duties. He noted that what Ziggy Blue had called "*fraud*" was actually "*under coding,*" which had been recognized as a problem among many Medical Departments in the State of Xenolina. *Under coding* means that staff could code more time to programs. In other words, it is the same as *underspending*.

In terms of *racial and cultural* issues, the investigator reported that while the Medical Department staff was diverse, accusations had been rumored that one staff had made the comment, "*Mexican clerks are a dime a dozen!*" There never was a source identified for the comment. In fact, the Kinder County Medical Department made every possible effort to recruit and retain Hispanic personnel. While the investigator stated that an investigation into this issue would be conducted by the Civil Rights Division of the Xenolina Office of Administrative Hearings, the issue fell by the wayside as there was never an investigative report made on the matter.

The investigator found no evidence of *"illegal drug use"* by staff in the Kinder County Medical Department.

Dr. Gomes had been accused of violating patient privacy rights—a HIPAA violation. That was simply another phony issue. There was one particular incident where Etum Sword, County Analyst, claimed that Dr. Gomes had publicly commented indicating that Servicious' daughter had been a patient at the Kinder County Medical Department. Dr. Gomes had commented in a letter to the Coterie that he was always happy to provide Medical Department services to his family—most recently, a flu shot to Servicious' daughter. Etum Sword and Servicious attempted to show that the statement demonstrated that Dr. Gomes had committed a breach of HIPAA.

The second and third county-funded investigation of the Kinder County Medical Department yielded similar findings. Essentially, findings were largely insignificant and the results were similar to findings in other Medical Departments throughout the State of Xenolina. It should be noted that in the third investigation that was conducted by an investigator from a Special School of Global Public Health, Servicious specifically asked the investigator to demonstrate that the Kinder County Medical Department was going to be over budget for the fiscal year. When the investigator reported his findings, no budget information appeared in the report. Servicious was livid! It should also be noted that during Dr. Gomes' 14-year tenure, the Medical Department never had a budget shortfall.

In spite of the fact that three separate investigations failed to find any fraud, illegal drug use among staff, improperly trained staff, nor any discriminatory practices in the Kinder County Medical Department, Servicious continued to demand that the Medical Department Board fire Dr. Gomes, and if the Board would not take that action, Dr. Gomes should resign. Why? Simply because Servicious didn't want Dr. Gomes occupying a position that Servicious' girlfriend, Ziggy Blue, was seeking.

Some weeks following the circus created by Servicious, the Special School of Global Public Health's investigator reported the budget information that Servicious had demanded on the Kinder County Medical Department. There was no budget shortfall. The review (investigation) actually found that the Medical Department had a budget surplus of $7,000 for the fiscal year in question. This issue soon faded away with all the other allegations.

Fortunately, throughout this terrible period of time—a long window of chaos—a majority of the Medical Department Board continued to support Dr. Gomes and the management of his department. Shortly after Ziggy Blue's TV appearance and Servicious' press conference, Dr. Gomes and the Medical Department Board Chairman met to discuss Kinder County Medical Department issues that had been mentioned in the TV interview. Dr. Gomes emphatically assured the Chairman that there was no basis for the allegations Ziggy Blue, in her ridiculous disguise, had spouted to the public. In fact, Dr. Gomes explained that the ulterior motive for the TV appearance was to impugn Dr. Gomes and his management and administration of the Kinder County Medical Department because Ziggy Blue craved the position of Medical Department Director for herself. Ziggy Blue had recently learned that Dr. Gomes was not going to support her in her quest to become Medical Department Director, and upon hearing Dr. Gomes' decision, Ziggy had gone ballistic! She and Servicious then immediately hatched a plan for Dr. Gomes' demise and they put their plan in motion to sabotage Dr. Gomes' stellar career.

While the Chairman assured Dr. Gomes that she would look into the matter, after approximately a half dozen more Medical Department Board meetings, the Chairman and Dr. Gomes, and other member of the Board met with the County Keeper. In that meeting the anonymous letters issue became so heated that, in the presence of all the other Board members, one member of the Board actually physically threatened Dr. Gomes. And that was not the only time that the particular Medical Department Board member had threatened violence. In the hallway, immediately following the adjournment of one meeting, he threatened a colleague on the Board, Constance Billingsly, who immediately had made it clear to him, in no uncertain terms, that she was not afraid of him. Later, in the parking lot, the same undisciplined Board member verbally threatened one of the Town of Marigold's beloved physicians, Dr. Harry Nehamiah. Not long after these events, the undisciplined Board member resigned from the Kinder County Medical Department Board.

Dr. Gomes, on multiple occasions informed the Kinder County Medical Department Board that he intended to retire. His decision had been   made shortly after Servicious' press conference. However, he stated it was not in the best interest of the Kinder County Medical Department for him to retire immediately because the County Keeper had indicated that Dr. Gomes' Executive Accountant's employment with Kinder County was in jeopardy. Dr. Gomes wanted to prevent this miscarriage of justice if at all possi- ble. One primary issue that Dr. Gomes wanted to see resolved was his Executive Accountant's eligibility for retirement since the County Keeper and County Analyst had told him that if his Executive Accountant would "*go away,*" then the Medical Department's troubles would disappear. Dr. Gomes told the Board Chairman that he would retire when his Executive Accountant was able to retire and that date was September 30th. With that decision in place, Servicious subsequently released a statement announcing that the Kinder County Medical Department's management had not committed fraud.

During this entire ordeal, Dr. Gomes had been under great pressure from Servicious and two other members of the Coterie to retire. Later on, the Medical Department Board Chairman joined the chorus requesting his resignation.

As a result of the constant stress, Dr. Gomes' physician recommended that he take medical leave for several weeks. Dr. Gomes had been on leave only a short time when he received a call from his office asking him, urgently, to return to work due to a serious medical incident in the dental clinic. Ziggy Blue had made another wrong decision while Dr. Gomes was on leave. In this particular situation, Ziggy had not followed appropriate protocol and had attempted to lie her way out of the problem when interviewed by the Medical Department Board. However, it was clear to a majority of the Board that Ziggy had taken steps to cover up her mistake.

RETIREMENT

Dr. Gomes had decided to retire from the Kinder County Medical Department on the date he had indicated. Following his exodus from the Kinder County Medical Department, Ziggy Blue submitted her application on two separate occasions for the position of Kinder County Medical Director. She was turned down both times because the Medical Director for the State of Xenolina rejected her application each time. She had been warned that she might lose her license and the Kinder County Acting Medical Director told her that she had not been exonerated just because the court case against her had been dismissed. The case had been dismissed because the County Keeper had not informed the Acting Medical Director that a hearing had been scheduled to consider Ziggy Blue's status in the Kinder County Medical Department. Because the Acting Medical Director had not attended the meeting was the only reason the judge had dismissed the case against Ziggy Blue.

The Acting Medical Director resigned not long after the trick had been played on him. In an open letter to the citizens of Kinder County he stated: *"I have never, in my 35 years of public [Medical] service, witnessed such a political cancer growing on a county that has the potential to cause great harm to preventive public [Medical] services in the community."* He further stated: *"I personally believe this situation seriously begs for an inquiry into the motivation of certain political leaders, and reflection as to whether such elected officials are truly acting in the best interest of what's right for... the citizens of Kinder County."*

Following the resignation of the Acting Kinder County Medical Director, five members of the nine Board members who were left on the Board resigned.

PART III

SERVICIOUS

Servicious was of the opinion that every new girl in town with any clout or status, real or imaginary, belonged to him. This was the attitude he had taken a few years back when Kinder County hired its first and only female County Keeper. The situation surrounding the new girl in town at that time got so hot between Servicious and another individual who had captured the new County Keeper's heart that Servicious was ready to attack the gentleman. The two men never agreed on anything following the appointment of the female County Keeper even though they both were members of the Coterie.

Oh, the female County Keeper was a handsome woman with head-turning good looks. She was tall, slender, and charismatic. But why two men who had wives of their own had the nerve to openly go after each other's throats over another woman defies common sense, knowing that as public officials they were constantly under public scrutiny. But common sense isn't very plentiful sometimes, especially where the opposite sex is involved.

Well, whatever might have happened was cut short when the lady County Keeper decided that Kinder County Government was not where she wanted to be. After a few months on the job, she resigned and returned to her place of abode before she had become adventuresome enough to give Kinder County a try.

NEPOTISM

Nepotism is defined as the unfair practice of a powerful person of giving jobs and other favors to relatives. Nepotism in the work force can mean increased opportunity for employment, attaining a job for which other applicants are more qualified, or being paid more than others who hold similar positions with equivalent essential functions. Nepotism is most common in small, family-run businesses and small town and local governments. Where nepotism is practiced, studies have demonstrated decreased morale and commitment from non-relative employees. This also includes negative attitudes toward employers who engage in such practice.

Servicious, who pretended to operate in a climate of transparency, fell deep into the nepotism pit when he hired his wife. Prior to that transgression

Servicious had pressured other Kinder County department keepers to hire some of his other relatives. Servicious held no compunction about flaunting his power or subtly threatening Kinder County employees to act on his commands or risk termination of employment.

When Servicious' wife found out about his shenanigans with Cleopatra, so it has been said, she made her own set of demands, one of which was that Servicious would give her (the wife) a job in the Waste Department so that she could personally keep an eye on Cleopatra to keep her away from Servicious. Whether that was going to work remained to be seen. Everyone knew that when Cleopatra sunk her hooks into a man, his voice would no longer his, but would belong to her. What a county! How could the citi- zens ever expect to have good government with these types of scenarios operating?

RAY RIVERS

With situations unfolding as they were in Kinder County, Ray Rivers, the County Keeper, was nothing more than a seat-warmer and a "yes man." Ray Rivers was strikingly handsome and, initially, openly congenial. However, he would soon learn that he was caught in a web of treachery or working in a hornet's nest where he was not actually the driver in Kinder County Government, even though that is the reason he had been hired. Although Ray was sitting in the driver's seat, Servicious made it quite clear to the new County Keeper that he was not to make a move on any level without Servicious' permission.

Ray Rivers was a kind-hearted individual who needed a job because he had a large family to support. So, no matter what the consequences, he was going to find a way to placate Servicious and Cleopatra and do whatever he possibly could to appease them. And since their ultimate goal was to be rid of Redhawk, Ray Rivers had to handle Redhawk with kid gloves. He would pretend to be interested in any requests Redhawk made for her department, knowing all the time that either he was going to deny the request or the Coterie was going to deny the request. As far as they were concerned, the Department of Alliance Activity was nothing but a drain on the county and the activities consisted primarily of *waste, fraud,* and *abuse.* Furthermore, in their opinion, the majority of people utilizing that department were poor, shiftless, lazy, lousy, trashy excuses of human beings. The Coterie held neither sympathy nor compassion for them, but would always turn a deaf ear to their needs and concerns because in the eyes of the Coterie they were worthless.

Ray Rivers, being new to the area, made a golden effort to become acclimated in communities throughout Kinder County. He found, however, that he could not go into any village or hamlet without first getting clearance from Servicious. Soon, the new County Keeper found that he and his family were somewhat alienated because after a while it became demeaning to have to ask another human being if it were OK to visit a certain family or attend a particular function.

The Coterie only concerned itself with the high and mighty, well-to-do, elite-minded, pseudo-rich. These were the people who they felt would vote for them, and getting re-elected was always the Coterie's primary concern. Because as long as they were in office, they could scheme and squander the taxpayers' money however they wanted to. While previous members of the Coterie had in the past hired several forward-thinking, visionary County Keepers, this new gang had resisted progressiveness and quashed many promising ideas because they were limited in knowledge due to the fact that the Coterie was dominated by locals whose motives were self-serving, and who really had a blatant disregard for the needs and desires of the people of Kinder County. And when confronted, this Coterie failed to acknowledge and accept the magnitude of its actions and the negative impact some of its members had on employees' and citizens' well-being. Ray Rivers was only useful to the Coterie to do its dirty work. The County Keeper did not know that once his usefulness had satisfied the Coterie, they were going to send him packing back to High Ground.

KEN SLY

When Ray Rivers landed the job as County Keeper in Kinder County by a vote of 3 to 2, before long he brought along what would become his partner in mismanagement of funds, Ken Sly as Fund Guardian. It didn't take very long after Ken Sly was hired for those working with him, and supposedly under his supervision, to learn that he was a fake public administrator. And unlike the handsome County Keeper, Ray Rivers, Ken Sly was an ordinary-looking man, of average height, with no particular features that would make him otherwise memorable. He had come from the private sector where he didn't have to answer to anyone in his role as fund guardian, and he was accustomed to barking orders to his underlings who were tasked with getting the job done while he vanished into parts unknown for extended   periods of time. He always disappeared under the pretense that he was attending a meeting of importance somewhere. So, among Kinder County employees, Ken Sly was known as the *invisible man*, except when he was hovering around a building filling his lungs with smoke. During his numerous *"smoke breaks,"* he seemed to enjoy having those with a similar habit join him in frivolous conversation.

Ken Sly would keep the door to his office locked so that his assistants had no access to any papers or files kept in his office when he was away—which was often. If by chance anyone got to peek in his office when he was entering or making an exit, stacks and stacks of documents could been seen covering his office floor. Some of those stacks were knee-high, and most of the documents appeared to be untouched. So, it would seem that as his mail was given to him, he never bothered to try and decipher any of it. He simply bellowed instructions to his staff and relied upon their knowledge and good judgment to get *his* job done. Well then, who was really minding the store? The stunt Ken Sly pulled on Servicious could have been hilarious except one had to wonder, given the outcome of this episode, whether Servicious was really blind, dumb, or a part of the scheme? And depending upon the conclusion one might draw, did any of the shenanigans have anything to do with   misappropriation of funds? Sometimes things are so obvious, they don't need to be stated or spelled out! They are hiding in plain sight.

Now, the partnership between Ray Rivers and Ken Sly became a partnership to behold. One knew very little about keeping a county, and the other knew even less about guarding funds. But they both talked a good game and fooled the Coterie, which wasn't hard to do, into believing that they were the best thing for Kinder County since the discovery of water. The Coterie was so blinded that it even gave the Fund Guardian an $11,000 raise and he wasn't even doing his job. Yet at the same time, Kinder County employees who were giving outstanding performances in their respective positions were not given salary increases. Imagine how Servicious covered up the incompetence of Ken Sly when he learned he and Kinder County had been duped by this character! But somehow it was all kept under wraps. And when the Fund Guard- ian left Kinder County with his tail between his legs, guess what? The Kinder County Coterie gave him a good reference and helped him land another job. Now, is there anything wrong with that picture? Per- haps some of the revenue that the Fund Guardian hid ended up in the hands of the *powers-that-be*?

MS. POINDEXTER

Cleopatra kept busy building a coalition of flunkies to use to destroy Redhawk. There was one who filled the role of the perfect pigeon: Ms. Poindexter. Ms. Poindexter was the youngest of a family of five girls. She always felt inferior to her older sib-lings because they were all successful attorneys and Poindexter was a college dropout. Nevertheless, Ms. Poindexter had managed to eke out a semi-successful career at the Department of Alliance Activity where she was employed as a case agent. The one thing Ms. Poindexter had in common with her more intelligent, successful sisters is she could concoct some tall tales— one of the requisites of being a successful mouth-piece, the chosen profession of the other four Poindexter sisters. Physically, Poindexter appeared to be healthy and in great shape. She was a very handsome woman, with smooth black skin and curly black hair. She stood approximately six feet tall and displayed a buxomed ordained body. Too bad her psyche was not as healthy as her physique.

During the hours she was at work, Poindexter was impeccably dressed—starched white or chambray blouses of a variety of pastel colors. Black, blue, or khaki slacks, spit-shined shoes, and expensive leather belts. She always wore a colorful scarf around her neck that usually complemented the colors of the rest of her outfit of the day. Off the job, her attire of choice consisted of camouflage pants, a black T-shirt, combat boots, and a balaclava in winter when the weather was cold. Otherwise, she would leave her head uncovered, but otherwise the outfit was always the same, indicating to most observers that she was a member of some unknown paramilitary group.

Poindexter's inferiority had by now been parlayed into an extreme hatred of successful women—especially those who occupied a higher link on the organizational chain of Poindexter's workplace. This placed Redhawk at the top of Poindexter's hit list. Early on, following Redhawk's appointment to the position of Director of Alliance Activity, Poindexter began to covertly act to influence others to develop negative feelings and form negative opinions of Redhawk. Poindexter would criticize the boss' success and popularity within the community and among staff and the client population. Statements such as, "She's not as smart as you think she is," were among Poindexter's favorite rants in describing her boss. Poindexter always thought she was being covert as she spewed her poison. However, people understood Poindexter's motives and intelligently ignored her, because everyone who dealt with her had at some point witnessed, or been a victim of her perfidy. Poindexter became known as the *"Fabricator."* Nevertheless, people took the time to inform Redhawk of Poindexter's actions.

While Poindexter appeared to have mastered the English language when using her poisonous tongue, she could not compose a decently written sentence. She was known to split verbs, dangle participles, misplace conjunctions—you name it! She did it! However, Poindexter, with all of her inadequacies felt that she should be the top dog at the DAA simply because she had been there the longest. Poindexter couldn't seem to grasp the fact that she didn't have what it takes to be a strong leader. Left to Poindexter, she would have violated every rule under the sun whenever a man came along and gave her some attention. She couldn't help being *attention starved* due to the fact that she felt deprived of attention because her parents doted on the four successful attorneys in the family.

Poindexter presented herself to the public as the ultimate, cooperative, accommodating employee—and in many ways she was. But the yearning inside of her to hurt other women overpowered and overshadowed her desire to do good, and thus the ugly behaviors prevailed and grew more menacing with each passing year. By the year 2013, Poindexter felt that she had planted enough destructive thoughts in her circle of associates with whom she felt shared her line of thinking that she was ready to execute her long-planned coup. She began by writing anonymous letters to the Coterie and its henchwoman, Cleopatra. In these letters, Poindexter invented the most detrimental canards possible against Redhawk. She essentially described Redhawk as a charlatan, embezzler, larcenist, lawbreaking criminal in Kinder County Government. Poindexter used all of these negative descriptions of Redhawk in order to create and build an atmosphere of hatred toward Redhawk.

In the beginning the Coterie dismissed the letters as actions taken by disgruntled clients, staff, or someone expressing their own extreme jealousy. However, the more the Coterie ignored the letters, the more vicious and angry Poindexter became. Poindexter became the Scheherazade of Kinder County. She recognized the evilness in Cleopatra and decided   to use Cleopatra as her tool of destruction.

Cleopatra, being void of knowledge relative to the Department of Alliance Activity, at the same time was searching for a mark to use to undermine Redhawk. So Cleopatra and Poindexter became allies—partners in scheming. Cleopatra began to coerce the Coterie to act on some of the misinformation that Poindexter was providing. The fact of the matter is that Cleopatra could lie with the same slick ease that Poindexter could. Those two seemed to have been joined in a conspiracy made in hell. Since Redhawk was a loyal public servant, Cleopatra had to create a plan of attack that was fail-safe. She began a witch hunt in search of some act of omission or commission on Redhawk relative to Redhawk's job responsibilities. Finding nothing, Cleopatra began writing a series of disciplinary letters for actions that were foreign to Redhawk and all officials who checked the work at the Department of Alliance Activity. They were trained and knew what to look for and could not grasp how Cleopatra could get away with railroading Redhawk, knowing how little Cleopatra knew about the organizational behavior of the DAA. However, Cleopatra had the support of not only the Coterie, but she was also supported by May Rhinestone, the People Recourse Director, and Shady Worm, the new County Keeper.

MAY RHINESTONE

Now, May Rhinestone was also a newcomer to Kinder County. Initially, she presented herself as a professional with a real concern for the well-be- ing of Kinder County employees. However, she soon learned the hidden agenda of the Coterie against employees that she had befriended, and for fear of falling out of the good graces of the Coterie, May Rhinestone quickly abandoned those friendships and began her comeuppance by gradually showing her dull, ugly side. Instead of sparkling and glittering like the pseudo-diamond that she pretended to be, she began to glow as much as mud. The change was so drastic that those who thought they knew her just a little and had established some camaraderie with May Rhinestone found themselves speechless over some of the actions she began to take. One thing they could be assured of was that Kinder County employees had no one in authority to stand up for them. If May was their best and only representative spokesperson, county employees were doomed.

One action May Rhinestone took to ensure she would not lose her lackey status with the Coterie was to join the ranks of Cleopatra in her effort to bring about Redhawk's demise. May Rhinestone allowed numerous People Recourse regulations to be violated. She turned a deaf ear to any defensive statements that clearly pointed out to her how Kinder County Employees' General Policies were being ignored in order to have misinformation and lies perpetrated against Redhawk in particular. May Rhinestone had left an organization where employee rights was a foreign term. As far as she was concerned, employers could do anything they wanted to demote or dismiss employees without any consequences to the employer. So, she transferred that line of thinking to the Coterie as a way of currying favor. So, when Cleopatra concocted phony reasons to inflict disciplinary action against Redhawk, May Rhinestone played along in total agreement. The charges were so outrageous that Redhawk hired an attorney as a combative measure. When the attorney wrote a letter to Shady Worm, the new County Keeper, and Etum Sword, the County Analyst, they never bothered to respond to   Redhawk's attorney. Their fear of Servicious was so intense that they wouldn't dare do anything to raise his ire. So, it appeared that Redhawk was doomed. It would be just a matter of time before Cleopatra would have written enough disciplinary letters to dismiss Redhawk on unfounded charges or cause Redhawk to take detrimental actions against her, or choose to retire.

The People Recourse Director, May Rhinestone, is supposed to be the individual to go to in order to settle disputes among management personnel and employees. But in this case, the People Recourse Director was a player in the conspiracy against Redhawk, leaving Redhawk no recourse for assistance against the trumped-up charges that the devious mind of Cleopatra and her partner Servicious had concocted, and May Rhinestone had condoned.

SHADY WORM

It has often been said that with certain characters, self-preservation is more important than doing the right thing. Shady Worm was one of those characters when it boiled down to saving himself versus railroading Redhawk.

A few years back, Shady Worm had flipped his career, leaving the California Department of Corrections where his focus had been on dogging inmates. In that system, he was an Intensive Officer Supervisor where he supervised only one person whose job was to conduct surveillance on those inmates who had left prison walls and had begun living under *house arrest*. This was an area that needed to be incorporated into the greater social scheme of things. But how did the experience of supervising one surveillance officer equip Shady Worm with the necessary skills   and knowledge required for supervising a large work force as County Keeper? In truth, it didn't! And maybe that's why Shady Worm floated from one county to another and another—because he wasn't good at performing the job of County Keeper.

So, perhaps Shady Worm could be excused for his unfair assessment and maltreatment of Redhawk in Kinder County. *Ignorance is no excuse!* Is there any correlation between supervising a corrections officer and managing a county? *We don't think so!* In the role of County Keeper, supervision has to be broadened to cover a multitude of areas—including managing personnel policies, principles, and ethics of a diverse work force. Obviously, from Shady Worm's lack of strength in these areas, he did not have the spine needed to speak out and heft himself up to Servicious' flagrantly wicked ways. Shady Worm had studied *Basic Public Personnel Law* and should have recognized all of the violations that were being committed against Redhawk. But fear prohibits many men from demonstrating strength in the face of opposition. Shady Worm was one of those men. Shady Worm had his orders from Servicious and Cleopatra to be rid of Redhawk, and Shady Worm was acting accordingly.

This was not Shady's first time breaking the law. He had done so in another county under different circumstances when he violated 143-318.3 because he failed to follow the Open Meeting Law. So, shady dealings were nothing new to Shady Worm. He was living up to his name—one more time.

ETUM SWORD

Etum Sword was a pleasant-appearing character with a jolly demeanor. On the surface, he was quite likeable, except for his under-handed dealings for the Coterie. Etum's jolly look was enhanced by his plumpness, and the fact that he loved to taste the dewberry wine that Kinder County is so famous for. Essentially, the idea that he loves to taste the sauce was often validated by the alcoholic aroma that permeated the air around him with every breath that Etum Sword exhaled.

Etum Sword was the epitome of a *"yes man."* It didn't take much to satisfy him—a carry-over of conditioning during his humble beginnings. A good analogy for Etum Sword was *"dancer"* because he had mastered the art of dancing around issues when he felt providing a straightforward, accurate response would jeopardize his employment contract with the Coterie. So, Etum Sword could be counted on to loquaciously deliver vague, meaningless summations to important questions. But since the Coterie was comfortable with this style, one would have to conclude that it was a strategy he had developed to mislead the people on behalf of the Coterie. And in situations where Etum felt his dance wasn't limber enough to misconstrue the truth, he simply failed to make an appearance.

Even though Etum was cloaked with the Coterie's protection and would not dare do anything to risk losing this status, he seemed to have a soft side that allowed him to emanate a bit of compassion at various times for whatever reasons.

THE COTERIE

Now, their plan might have appeared simple, but it held grave implications for Redhawk. Because the Coterie not only wanted to be rid of Redhawk, they did not want to have to pay an equitable retire- ment salary for a female who had served more than 30 years as Director of Alliance Activity. So, the plan was to fire Redhawk and effectively cause the loss of all Kinder County benefits. What sort of people were running Kinder County?

Because the Coterie didn't yet know that Red- hawk had filed charges with the Equal Employment Opportunity Commission (EEOC) of age and race discrimination, the Coterie gave Cleopatra free rein to inflict the ultimate humiliation on Redhawk. They intended to destroy her! Emasculate her! Take away her dignity! Reduce her to a mental case! The action they used to try and accomplish this was to, first of all, place Redhawk on *"Investigatory Leave."* Investigatory Leave? When this ploy was used against Redhawk she had no idea what the scheme was all about. Redhawk had done nothing for which she should be sent home. It all happened out of the blue. Cleopatra and May Rhinestone called Redhawk into a conference and asked a few questions about some equipment that had been requested with Cleopatra's approval. As it turned out, Redhawk was in a no-win situation at this point. If Redhawk had resisted and questioned their decision, they would have cited her with a charge of insubordination. Redhawk was left with no choice except to follow the Coterie's orders. Redhawk instantly made a wise decision not to ask them any questions. The Coterie had felt that given enough time it would find something, any little thing, that Redhawk had done so Cleopatra and May Rhinestone went to work digging for dirt in order to justify placing Redhawk on *"Investigatory Leave."*

Initially, they told Redhawk she was being sent home for 10 days. But Cleopatra and May Rhinestone emphasized that *"this is not disciplinary action"*! Oh, no? Well what kind of action is it when an employee is being sent home for no apparent reason? Is there a technical term that applies? What about *"sheer meanness*"? Of course, it wasn't disciplinary, because Redhawk had not done anything to warrant this maltreatment. But the general public did not know this. And once the negative action had been taken, the assumption was that Redhawk had committed some egregious act, because who gets sent home for nothing? It only happened if you happened to be an employee in Kinder County Government whom Servicious and the Coterie didn't want as an employee in local government.

Cleopatra used lies and innuendoes from disgruntled individuals and DAA employees as an excuse to probe into Redhawk's personal life. Imangine that! They had all of Redhawk's personnel information in their files, so it was easy for May Rhinestone to release it to be used to probe into bank accounts to see if there were funds being channeled into to Redhawk's accounts. Funds that had been stolen from Kinder County that would have substantiated claims from Servicious and others that Redhawk was committing *fraud*. They even stripped the computer on Redhawk's desk of all information to see if Redhawk had used Kinder County equipment for personal use. Finding nothing, they began to examine the programs administered at the Department of Alliance Activity to see if Redhawk had found a way to steal medicine or food through certain programs, or if she had some cohorts operating with her to get kickbacks from clients. *They should have examined themselves!*

Of course, this probing and searching could not be completed within 10 days, so Redhawk received a certified letter at home informing her that the period of her *investigatory leave* had been extended. This was to give the Coterie and Cleopatra more time to *complete their "witch hunt."*

By this time there was a *"media frenzy"* of curious reporters contacting Redhawk and inquiring as to the reason she was placed on leave and why the leave was being extended. It seemed so feeble when Redhawk tried to convince them that she, herself, didn't know why she had been sent home, nor what they were investigating. Redhawk was as curious as the public, but *dared* not ask the Coterie any questions—again, for fear of being cited for *insubordination.* Because in the first place, when someone is being sent home from his or her job, they should be told why they are being sent home.

On the day Redhawk was sent home, she had only been given the following orders: (1) Don't talk to staff; (2) Do not communicate with clients; and (3) Do not leave home unless under special circumstances <u>with our permission</u>! In other words, Redhawk was essentially under *"House Arrest."* For what? God only knows! Because, until this very day, Redhawk has never been given any explanation nor a reason for what they had done to her. The reality is, they felt that they did not have to have a reason. They were simply exercising their *"power"*! And, of course, when entities feel that they are *"untouchable,"* they feel that their power is *"absolute!"* Which gives them the right to abuse power, and in doing so, abuse people. Redhawk is just one example, albeit one of the most blatant examples, because there have been numerous others, but none this extreme. And in all those other cases, they had been given the courtesy of knowing what offense(s) they were being accused of.

CONCERNED CITIZENS
& REDHAWK SUPORTERS

While there were people gloating at the unwarranted negative actions the Coterie had taken against Redhawk, there was a multitude of individuals and groups who were making inquiries and taking ac- tion to boomerang some troubles back to the Cote- rie. They were calling Redhawk, visiting her, meeting with groups on her behalf, and consulting with mem- bers of the legal profession in other states. There was no trepidation in the midst of these supporters. Many of them were angry and vowed not to let the Coterie get away unscathed with this *power play* they had inflicted.

One group decided to appeal to the Coterie as professionals and concerned citizens to see if they could get an inkling of the Coterie's intentions or the next step in the abuse they were inflicting upon Redhawk. Since there was no egregious offense that Redhawk had committed, everyone concerned was flummoxed over what appeared to be a grave mistake on the Coterie's part. Redhawk addressed each of those supporters who was geared up to approach the Coterie at one of its public meetings.

First of all, Redhawk provided assurance to her supporters that there was nothing in her back- ground during her more than 30-year tenure as DAA Director that could surface and embarrass anyone for speaking on her behalf. She assured them, too, that there was nothing she had done that warranted the harsh discipline that—even though Cleopatra and May Rhinestone assured Redhawk it was non-disciplinary—the Coterie was allowing to be set up against her. (*At this juncture, she had been sent home for 10 days initially, and then an additional 30 days on top of that.*) Redhawk expressed to her supporters her belief that Cleopatra had spent, and was continuing to spend, this time on a "*witch hunt*" searching for reasons to terminate her employment, one reason being Cleopatra's insecurity at being boss over something that she knew nothing about. The second reason being the Coterie wanted to rob Redhawk of benefits she had earned from being a long-standing, devoted Kinder County employee. There were other reasons, too, but since they were obvious to anyone looking on, those reasons need not be mentioned.

Redhawk supporters understood that in the entire history of Kinder County Government such a tactic had never been used in an attempt to force the retirement of a competent, loyal employee. Redhawk knew, and her supporters felt, that if Cleopatra and the Coterie had something concrete against her, they would simply have called her into a dismissal conference and terminated her employment. It would not have taken more than 40 whole days of paid leave to make a simple decision.

A management-directed investigation that is based on *"hearsay* and *inuendos,"* speculation or otherwise, is no justification for sending an employee home for more than a month when that employee doesn't even know what is being investigated or why she is being placed on *"paid leave"* under the guise of an investigation. People lie all the time. So, was this action by the Coterie setting a precedent that every time anyone fabricates a good tale on an employee that employee will be sent packing, all the while getting paid to do nothing?

Initially, phone calls and texts were fielded incessantly. People were not just curious, they wanted to know what Redhawk had done. What crime(s) had she committed that she would be so blatantly sent home without having been given any valid reason for the Coterie's actions against her? They asked if the Coterie could do that and get away with it? Everyone was thinking that was not possible, so Redhawk must have committed some egregious infraction or un-imaginable crime. At least that's the way it appeared to onlookers, and they were not about to cease making inquiries until they knew the untold story.

Yes, friends and relatives were supportive—most of them. But this turn of events was so unreal that there was a real "*need-to-know*" hanging in the balance. Even Redhawk's pastor stated to Redhawk, *confidentially*, that it was OK to talk about it because she was there to assist Redhawk if Redhawk was in trouble. So, the question was raised and the statements made: "What have you done? It must have been something! They can't just do this to you when you haven't done anything but perform the essential functions and responsibilities of your job, can they?"

To these questions Redhawk responded, once again: "Yes, it appears that they can because this is what they have done."

ELLERBY WATTS

Throughout this ordeal, Redhawk was relying on the advice of her attorney. He practiced primarily in an adjoining county, which meant it was not a great inconvenience for Redhawk to travel to his office. It was virtually impossible for Redhawk to retain legal representation in Kinder County because she was in a battle with the County Kinder establishment.

Although he came from humble beginnings, Redhawk's attorney, Ellerby Watts, was destined for success early in life. His performance from the time he entered school was outstanding. In college his leadership skills were evident in the classroom as well as observed in the extra-curricular activities in which he took part. He was captain of the debate team and while attending law school at Case Western Reserve, he was president of his class. Following graduation from law school, Ellerby married his college sweetheart and became a family man. He was a family man whose family values were in sync with those of the American dream. He was a husband, father, grandfather, good neighbor and friend. He loved his community and in his spare time engaged in civic and community activities designed to build a better America. He held memberships in the Association of the American Association for Justice, the American Bar Association, and actively participated in the Criminal Justice Policy Program. He was a member of the Omega Psi Phi Faternity, Inc., wherein he engaged in humanitarian projects. Additionally, Ellerby Watts donated his legal expertise to the community as Attorney for the Guardian ad Litem Program, serving children and families in the Foster Care System. He also coached Little League baseball for 15 years. He was always highly respected and was a gentle soul whose Christian values and beliefs guided his negotiations with the Kinder County Coterie.

Ellerby Watts was not only appalled by the situation Redhawk was expounding to him, he found it impossible to believe. Perhaps this was because he, too, had served several terms as a member of the Coterie Board in his home county, as well as serving in the position of Chairman of the Coterie for the entire State of Xenolina. So, he was well aware of applicable personnel policies, rules, and federal laws that provided a degree of protection to government employees. Not to belabor the point, but he was astounded by the things he was hearing. So, in his southern gentlemanly fashion, he made attempts to reason with the Coterie, requesting fair and equal treatment for his client so as not to proceed any further with Redhawk's grievance against them. He wrote in one comuniqué to the Coterie, County Keeper, and County Analyst: *"My client is a good steward in her church and community. Anyone who witnesses her mannerism and carriage, and her interaction with her surroundings, will tell you that her character is good. She presents herself as the ultimate professional, and untold numbers of individuals and groups with whom she interacts will testify to this declaration. I find no statements in the written warning that cite unacceptable personal conduct. No use of profanity, no disrespect shown to anyone, no obscene actions or expressions, and no instances of insubordination."* The Coterie and its cohorts did not care about the truth Ellerby Watts was presenting to them on Redhawk's behalf or in Redhawk's defense. The Coterie treated him as if he were an invisible man.

Redhawk had filed a written grievance with Shady Worm, the County Keeper, but soon learned that she had wasted her time. Shady Worm gave

Redhawk an appointment to meet with him and Etum Sword, Kinder County's Analyst, to voice her details of the grievance in order for Shady Worm to make a fair and impartial decision. What a joke! If Redhawk had any notion that Shady Worm was going to decide in favor of the truth versus going against Servicious, Cleopatra and the Coterie, she was sadly mistaken.

HEARING

On the day of the scheduled hearing, Etum Sword failed to appear. Shady Worm offered some feeble excuse for Etum's absence that even Shady himself did not believe. So Shady served as a *"one-man grievance committee."* Do you understand what is being said here? How could a fearful wimp make an honest ruling if it meant he might lose his job on the spot?

Well, anyway, Shady sat and pretended to listen to Redhawk and at the end of the *"pseudo-hearing"* told Redhawk that he would take all the facts into consideration and render a decision within five days. What facts? He didn't take notes during the *"pseudo-hearing,"* he made no recording of the ses- sion! And he certainly is no genius with a memory so great that he could recall every word that Redhawk had stated. That would have been impossible even if he were a genius because he wasn't even listening to a word Redhawk was saying. He appeared bored and simply sat in the room just so he could say he had followed personnel procedure. But the final decision in Redhawk's case had been made long before he entered the room.

When the decision letter from Shady Worm arrived on the fifth day following the *"pseudo-hearing,"* Shady stated in so many words that Redhawk could suck up the truth and do things Cleopatra's way because her word was final—even though she didn't know anything about DAA programs and operations—and he was not going against her. In other words, he acted as if Cleopatra was his boss and he had been given orders not to rock the boat.

Neither Redhawk nor her attorney was surprised at Shady Worm's decision. In Shady's letter he had the nerve to state that his decision was final and there was no right to appeal his decision. No provisions for appealing his decision? Are you kidding me? We know that Shady was no genius, but everyone knows that in government only the word of the Supreme Court is final. So who did this little man working in little old Kinder County think he was? A Supreme Court Justice?

Since Redhawk had also filed a discriminatory complaint with the Equal Employment Opportunity Commission (EEOC), the next real step in the process was to wait on a decision from the EEOC.

The EEOC is the federal agency responsible for enforcing employment discrimination laws. These laws protect employees against a number of discriminatory actions in the workplace. This includes, *"harassment by managers, co-workers, or others in the workplace who commit discriminatory acts because of race, color, religion, sex and gender identity, national origin, age (40 or older), disability or genetic information."* Also included is *"retaliation for having complained about job discrimination, or assisted with a job discrimination investigation or lawsuit. An individual may also file a charge on behalf of another person in order to protect the aggrieved person's identity.* There are a number of limitations associated with filing a complaint—one of which is the time limitation for getting the complaint filed and on record. Redhawk had filed within the allowed window.

With this being said, Redhawk, upon advice from her legal counsel, was not in a position to feed any details of the *"investigatory leave fiasco"* to her friends and family. While many of them were angry about the situation, Redhawk had to display a demeanor that reverberated a sense of peace and calm so that friends and family would follow her lead. Everyone was inquiring about what might they do to help in the situation, and Redhawk emphasized that her attorney had the situation under control.

PROTESTS

.

Large groups threatened a protest march, but Redhawk discouraged that action. The Coterie was not the sort of entity that understood logical reasoning, so any approach would have been a waste of time. Any group that blatantly ignores an attorney who is trying to reason with them certainly isn't going to give any consideration to what it looks down upon as trouble from underlings.

Although many times following the unfair and unwarranted suspension Redhawk felt great anger toward Cleopatra and the Cotrie—especially the People Recourse Director who knew that the entire scenar- io surrounding Redhawk's suspension was staged to cover up the Coterie's deep desire to expel Redhawk from the job she was performing as DAA Director—Redhawk was able to control herself because she was a woman of great discipline. And because so many friends and supporters were constantly praying with and for her, and everyone knew that the outcome of this fiasco would be positive because there was no evidence that would allow the situation to end negatively. At this juncture, Redhawk was channeling her energy in a positive direction as opposed to delving into recriminations.

Because Redhawk was not publicly speaking out in her own defense and many staff members were speaking out on her behalf some staff hinted to Redhawk that she was abandoning them. However, Redhawk assured them that that was not the case.

Redhawk specifically stated that since she was currently suspended—albeit without justification—from work, it would be inappropriate for her to engage in rants about the unfair treatment and actions of Cleopatra and the Coterie. When staff who were making preparations to leave the DAA agency because they felt their employer—the Kinder County Coterie—was no longer worthy of their dedication. Many of them asked Redhawk for job references for their new potential employers. Often Redhawk had to explain the awkwardness of providing references while she was on suspension because other employers, not knowing the truth of her current situation, might feel that she was unworthy and not in a position to make honest recommendations about her staff's job performance. This would not have been in the applicant's favor. Redhawk asked DAA staff to try to be understanding.

During the period of suspension, some days strangers would come to Redhawk's door using various disguises. Not knowing their intentions, most days Redhawk refused to answer the door because it was not her custom to open the door to uninvited strangers. Furthermore, since there was a "so-called" or *pseudo-investigation* underway for which Cleopatra and the Coterie had never given Redhawk a reason, it was unlikely that Redhawk was going to, in any way, assist them if this were the reason for those "stranger" visits.

Some days were ordinary with a few telephone calls from friends and supporters, numerous Facebook posts from staff, and other contacts from strangers or people with whom Redhawk was not familiar, but who nevertheless offered to assist if they could. Reading the Facebook posts and words of wisdom about life's mysteries helped to pass the time away.

As days moved on to weeks, and weeks were approaching a month, Redhawk continued to receive phone calls, texts, emails, and visits from people who were baffled by the situation and trying to gain an understanding of the boldness of Cleopatra and the Coterie's discriminatory actions against her. They wanted to know, in addition to the unfairness of placing Redhawk on paid leave for no valid reason, how long could or would they continue to extend the leave without any explanation whatsoever as to the reason, or reasons, why. Finding answers to this question was going to be an enormous challenge. A lack of understanding can produce tension, impatience and frustration. Emotional urgency was escalating because there were no clear answers as to why this situation materialized in the first place. Talk about *"transparency?"* This was just another example of Cleopatra and the Coterie's murky leadership style.

One doctor, a friend of the Hawk family residing in Washington, D.C., called and asked how arrogant could Servicious continue to be, since the doctor knew firsthand, according to him, that Servicious was driving the *"destructive train"* for Kinder County Government. The doctor advised Redhawk to have her attorney do something to stop this madness as it was so unacceptable in the 21st century. He asked what they—Cleopatra and the Coterie—were looking for. And Redhawk assured him that she had no clue. But whatever it was, it could not have been related to her job performance because her work was greater than satisfactory and an in-depth look at DAA records would validate this claim.

When the doctor asked Redhawk about her performance evaluations, he was assured that her performance evaluations had all been *very good, excellent, and outstanding* throughout her entire career as DAA Director. All performance evaluations had been conducted by the DAA Boards over a period of more than 31 years. As a matter of fact, Redhawk pointed out that during the two-year period since the responsibility of evaluating her had been taken away from the DAA Board and handed to Cleopatra, Director of the Waste Department, that Cleopatra *had never once* conducted a performance evaluation of Redhawk.

There were several reasons for this, according to Redhawk. One was that Cleopatra knew *zilch* about the Department of Alliance Activity. Everyone knows that it is extremely difficult--virtually impossible--to evaluate an individual's job performance when you have neither knowledge nor understanding of the job being performed. Secondly, Cleopatra felt she did not have to evaluate Redhawk's job performance because she had been hired to get rid of Redhawk, and she had ways of doing that without being concerned about whether or not Redhawk did her job. Cleopatra did not care about the essential functions of the   job being carried out because she thought nothing of the client population that was served by the Department of Alliance Activity.

To further accomplish her mission, Cleopat- ra called upon a faithless entity that presented itself as an auditor of programs for the State of Xenolina. It was known as Program Evaluators and Finishers. This entity lacked human resources with the necessary knowledge and skills to evaluate all the DAA agencies in the state. It was sought by Cleopatra and the Coterie to practice on Kinder County. In other words, Kinder County was the *guinea pig*. The lead program evaluator was told that all he needed to do was state in no uncertain terms that Kinder County did not need a DAA Director. And once Cleopatra was rid of Redhawk, she would wait a period of one year and then hire a DAA Director who was as unknowledgeable and unskilled in working DAA programs as she was. Then Cleopatra would not feel so threatened by a director under her supervision as she had felt having Redhawk in the position.

However, when the program evaluator made his report on the DAA in Kinder County, *nothing*, I repeat, *nothing*, was found out of order or below acceptable standards in the manner in which the Kinder County DAA was being administered by Redhawk and the DAA Management Team. But Cleopatra didn't care about that report. She had a mission to accomplish.

All of the worthwhile and meaningful suggestions contained in the report had already been made by Redhawk years and months before this *witch hunt* evaluation took place. Suggestions that had been made by Redhawk to improve efficiency at the DAA were blatantly ignored by the Coterie because any advice from Redhawk was unwelcomed, good or otherwise.

The Program Evaluation and Finisher report did not produce or offer anything to warrant Redhawk's loss of employment as DAA Director. And although Cleopatra was extremely disappointed, Redhawk was not going to quit.

Cleopatra, in collusion and conjunction with May Rhinestone, People Recourse Director, had long ago decided that all she needed to do was write a series of *warning letters* to Redhawk and place them in Redhawk's personnel file, and Redhawk would be *history.* So having been placed in the position of Redhawk's supervisor for less than six months, Cleopatra wrote the first *warning letter* in March 2014. She penned a second *warning letter* in April 2015. And the third *warning letter* Redhawk received was in June 2015 wherein Cleopatra and May Rhinestone assured Redhawk that the whole reason for being sent home on "*Investigtory Leave*" was not disci- plinary, and the letter never stated *what was being investigated* or why the leave was designated as *investigatory leave*. The entire matter was conflicting and devoid of common sense. But again, that's the way Cleopatra and the Coterie operated—in a manner that was often devoid of common sense.

TEAMWORK

The fact that Redhawk was leading in a county where she was reared and occupying a leadership role for people and families, many of which she knew very well, intensified her desire to take all possible actions to help build a better community—to make life better for the people that she knew and loved, and people who felt they could rely and depend on her to put forth her honest and best efforts to serve relentlessly within the bounds of the laws and regulations governing the Department of Alliance Activity to the best of her ability. Such a notion made it easy for Redhawk to initiate and manage organizational changes as the need arose. Her style of communicating openly with staff and seeking staff, and sometimes community input, when needed to implement new policies and procedures, served to enable Redhawk to manage the Department of Alliance Activity heretofore successfully.

With the cooperation of the State of Xenolina, and support of the Board of Alliance Activity and the DAA Management Team and staff, Redhawk was able to create a learning organization through numerous and constant training activities, garner community support when major changes were necessary at the DAA agency, and collaborate and coordinate activities with other agencies impacted by proposed changes. Redhawk felt that her ability as a "moderate conserver" enabled her to provide clear structure in ambiguous situations; her appreciation and acknowledgment of contributions of co-workers; and her desire for unity within DAA were all positives that enabled and empowered her to initiate and manage organizational change.

So, even though Redhawk was perplexed by the disparaging actions of Cleopatra and the Coterie, she was mentally equipped with the knowledge and grit to cope with the stunt they were pulling. As a matter of fact, she had warned DAA staff and the now disbanned DAA Board that this was going to happen because the devious plan had been shared with Redhawk many times by so many different reliable sources.

As the days wore on, and questions remained

unanswered, the visits to Redhawk, phone calls, texts and emails continued to flood in, and plans continued to be made in preparation for confronting the Coterie during a public forum.

Redhawk's supporters felt this was a matter where dissatisfaction with Cleopatra's and the Coterie's tactics should be publicly voiced. And when they spoke before the Coterie, their expositions were going to be accurately and expertly delivered.

On Sunday afternoon, the eve before the people were going to address the Coterie in a public forum, Redhawk had a surprise visitor. It was one of those beautiful Sunday afternoons where many country folks relax, engage in easy, light conversations with family and friends and reminisce about earlier events, be it recent weeks, months ago or years ago, or yesterday.

While Redhawk, her spouse, Jay Hawk, and some visiting friends were sitting outside on the steps relaxing and engaging in idle chat, the moment was pleasantly interrupted when one of the communi- ty's most outstanding and leading icons stopped by. Mr. Jess Freeman, a renowned orator, professor, administrator, and global community leader, by his presence created an instant of astonishment for both Redhawk and her visiting friends when he stepped

out of his shiny Lincoln Continental. Since Mr. Freeman was at the time spending a while temporarily at
a local facility for dignitaries, it was unusual for him
to leave the group on a Sunday afternoon. Redhawk
was overjoyed to have him visit because that one visit
uttered loud and clear how important it was to expose
to the general public the efforts that were being made
by Cleopatra and the Coterie to discredit her and the
work she had performed so professionally with tremendous dignity throughout her tenure as DAA Director.

Mr. Freeman had been a coach and mentor for
Redhawk from the moment she had been appoint- ed
to the position of Director of Alliance Activity for
Kinder County. He had followed her administration
of public programs, fair and professional treatment of
staff, and compassionate delivery of service to clients
throughout the more than 30 years she had been a
public servant in Kinder County. During this particular visit he stated that he wanted to join the group of
speakers who were scheduled to address the Coterie
Board the following evening, because he had insight
about Redhawk's dedication and efficiency as a public
administrator that needed to be interpolated for public consumption during this critical period of confu-
sion and enormous challenges relative to Redhawk's
credibility.

While Redhawk was deeply touched by Mr. Freeman's gesture of kindness and altruism, she assured him that the speakers who were geared up for the Coterie's meeting would articulate clearly and convey with confidence the message that needed to be delivered and understood. It was conventional wisdom that brought Mr. Freeman and Redhawk to a mutual agreement on the fact that he should coach her and the group, but should distance himself from the uproar that could possible surface during the meeting. Because although all participants would be courteous and respectful, the behavior and demeanor of Servicious was unpredictable. As it turns out—which could not have been foreseen at the time of the conversation—Servicious was so angry and childish when the meeting took place and the public forum began, he walked out. Good riddance!

PUBLIC FORUM

July 27, 2015, was one of those beautiful lazy days of summer where the southern morning dew had kissed the green grass. Where warm sunshine showered everyone who ventured outdoors. Where birds were singing sweet melodies and flowers were looking up to the heavens. It was another great day to behold the wonders of life. It was also the day of the Coterie meeting in which many Kinder County citizens were poised to attend the public forum later that day.

As the day moved into evening, all speakers were prepared and ready to address the Coterie. Each speaker had signed up to speak prior to the beginning of the meeting and were anxiously raring to get to the podium.

Mack Strozer was the first speaker to address the Coterie and the audience. Mack was quite an effervescent guy who was well-known to the Coterie. Mack had, on previous occasions, addressed the Coterie numerous times in his quest to bring recreation for youths into Kinder County. Mack could never understand how the Kinder County Coterie could waste tax dollars on an abundance of unnecessary items, but would only spend on recreation for the easternmost section of Kinder County. Mack reminded the Coterie that his plight to bring recreation to communities in central and western Kinder County had not changed. But he made it clear that that was not his purpose for appearing before the Coterie this time.

Following a few more opening statements about himself pointing out that he was currently campaigning to win a seat on the Marigold Town Council, he finally stated his reason for making an appearance at the public forum. Mack stated that citizens from around Kinder County were there because they were concerned about Redhawk and the maltreatment she was receiving from Cleopatra and the Coterie. He stated that onlookers were perplexed, and begged the Coterie to provide some answers for communities and citizens throughout Kinder County.

Mr. Strozer pointed out that Redhawk was a diligent employee and had served the county for years with unquestionable dedication. He reminded the Coterie that she was smart and had saved Kinder County millions of dollars over the years by being an efficient public administrator, and this could be verified through an examination of public records. He wanted to know if Redhawk had done anything criminal. Which was really a rhetorical question because everyone knew that if she had committed a crime, she would have been taken into custody, locked up, and the media would have had a field day with Redhawk and whatever charges had been brought against her. There were no charges, so that answered the question.

Mr. Strozer pointed out that even some criminals don't always lose their job. So, what was the problem here, he wanted to know? He turned to the only female on the Coterie Board, Daisy Keystone who, by the way, was the newest member of the Coterie and was not caught up in their shenanigans. Ms. Keystone was quick to respond that she supported Redhawk 100 percent. That single statement probably sealed Ms. Keystone's fate for the upcoming election in which Ms. Keystone would have to run in order to retain the seat she occupied on the Coterie Board. Because Servicious was out to get Redhawk, he would definitely pull every string possible to defeat

Daisy Keystone to remove any semblance of support Redhawk might have had from one of his colleagues. Ms. Keystone stated that to her knowledge there was nothing Redhawk had done wrong, and Ms. Keystone herself wanted answers, too. She also pointed out, however, that the situation was a personnel matter at this juncture, and the Coterie was not at liberty to discuss it. Daisy Keystone had always promoted transparency throughout the years she had been engaged in public service. She had put forth diligent efforts to ensure that Kinder County Public Schools would not be shortchanged when funds were allocated to various departments in Kinder County Government. She reminded Mack Strozer that if the matter could be discussed openly without violating personnel policy, she would surely enlighten the public with as much as she knew—which was very little—about Redhawk's treatment by Kinder County officials.

That being said, Mack Strozer suggested that it would be wise and prudent to ask Redhawk to return to the job. After all, he said, she would be retiring in a year or two anyway.

The second speaker of the evening was Dr. Raquel Stone, an exciting personality who powerfully projected herself into issues where individuals   had been denigrated by entities and individuals such as Cleopatra and the Coterie had perpetrated against Redhawk in the situation at hand. Dr. Stone was also known throughout Kinder and surrounding counties as a great negotiator, facilitator, and coordinator of numerous conferences and seminars that brought people together to improve social and political policies and practices. At this particular forum, Dr. Stone's focus was the *maltreatment of Redhawk.*

Dr. Stone cited a letter from Cleopatra to Redhawk in which Cleopatra wolfed some orders that included orders for Redhawk not to return to the Department of Alliance Activity (a public building); not to contact staff; and not make contact with clients. (*Why would Redhawk have had the need to make contact? She was no longer working daily. She was on paid leave.*) Further, Dr. Stone pointed out that Redhawk had been told that the reason she was being placed on leave was "*non-disciplinary.*" Then what was the reason for telling her she could not function normally if it wasn't disciplinary? Dr. Stone emphasized that, in essence, Cleopatra and the Coterie had placed Redhawk "*under house arrest.*" What on earth for? Nobody knew! Redhawk, herself, had not been given an explanation.

Dr. Stone told Cleopatra and the Coterie that they (Redhawk supporters) were not going back to

"Jim Crow" days. She reminded them that the workplace was no place to engage in personal vendettas. And she questioned why Cleopatra seemed to have such hatred for Redhawk? Fear of Redhawk's knowledge? Cleopatra's lack of understanding of an agency over which she had been given responsibility? Dr. Stone told the Coterie and Cleopatra that they owed Redhawk an apology and that they should call Redhawk and instruct her to return to work.

Bianca Behal was the next speaker who expressed her feelings and opinion with tremendous passion. Bianca, of Puerto Rican descent, spoke in a musical tone, accentuating each statement in a staccato manner that drew attention to every word. Bianca, a beautiful young woman, always drew attention whenever she entered a room because she was blessed with eye-catching, head-turning, good looks. So when she stepped up to the podium, she held everyone's undivided attention.

Bianca referred to Redhawk with the utmost respect. She emphasized how Redhawk, as a lead- er, had fought for staff to gain resources necessary to serve clients efficiently and effectively. She addressed some of the training Redhawk had provided for them, especially Redhawk's teachings on treatment of clients—how staff should respect clients and minimize the appearance of being an intrusion in clients' lives.

Bianca noted that the Department of Alliance Activity was now being micromanaged by one, Cleopatra, who was ill-equipped for the job of managing the DAA. Bianca stated that she didn't even know Cleopatra, had never seen Cleopatra, yet Cleopatra was in a sense terrorizing staff because everyone at the DAA felt that Cleopatra, by her unprofessional behavior, was out to terminate DAA staff's employment.

Lastly, Bianca told the Coterie that she felt she would lose her employment by speaking on Redhawk's behalf, but she told them they would just have to fire her because she needed to voice her concern, and that she was resonating the sentiments of the majority other DAA staff.

Ms. Behal was followed by Derrick Powers, who had at one time been a member of the Coterie Board. But that was back in the day when the Co- terie actually dedicated themselves to serving Kinder County citizens instead of themselves.

Mr. Powers emphasized that he had served on the DAA Board for eight years and worked closely with Redhawk. During that time he said Redhawk always knew the intergral parts of each program administered at the DAA, was always efficient, and not once was there ever a time when federal, state, or county level reviews were incorrect. Mr. Powers stated that

Redhawk always presented herself and DAA reports in a most professional manner, and overall operated the agency professionally. He stated that Redhawk has enjoyed an impeccable career, and in terms of an investigation, he suggested it would be wise to investigate the *"investigator."* Mr. Powers stated that the situation Cleopatra and the Coterie had created needed to be examined very closely. Mr. Powers reiterated that the job of public servants was to care for and provide an element of protection for the less fortunate members of society. And in this particular instance, it would be a good idea to investigate the *"investigator."*

Also among the speakers was the enormously influential Retired General Clement Stanton. Over the years he had been able to energize citizens in communities all over Kinder County to engage in various ground-breaking projects that improved activities of daily living for children through better schools, and improved recreational activities for all demographic groups. Additionally, he had served on the Coterie Board following his retirement from the military, and in that role, together he and his colleague on the Board, Derrick Powers, collaboratively acquired federal grants that improved housing, and subsequently living standards, for Kinder County's low-income families.

All of his life, the General had been a shaker and a mover. If he were wind, he would have been a tornado. Had he been a wave, he would have been a tsunami. In other words, he was a man with a lot of power. Power he used positively and constructively to achieve success in all of his undertakings. Power born out of the fact that he possessed great intelli- gence and used it wisely.

General Stanton, although he had traveled and lived in countries world-wide, was a Kinder County native. Following his illustrious military career, he returned to Kinder County and submerged himself in community affairs.

As he addressed the Coterie, General Stanton expounded on the worth of a public servant, point- ing out that Kinder County employees are the govern- ment's most valuable asset. He said he was appalled by the hostile work environment that the Coterie had created. He emphasized that there had never in 33 years been an instant where Redhawk and the De- partment of Alliance Activity had received an unsat- isfactory rating. As a matter of fact, all ratings had ranged from satisfactory to outstanding—mostly out- standing. He reminded the Coterie to review person- nel policies, treat staff fairly, and pay them a decent salary in order to curtail turnover. Like Derrick Pow- ers, General Stanton asked the Coterie to look very closely at the investigation because what had been stated was in direct conflict with the actions Cleopatra and the Coterie had taken against Redhawk.

Another speaker, Woodson Dobgood, was a man who had no compunction about being truthful with expressing his dissatisfaction and disappointment over the manner in which the Coterie had railroaded Redhawk by sending her home for no justifiable or conceivable reason. Charismatic and dedicated to serving his fellowman, Woodson never shied away from any imbroglio where he felt his input could make a positive difference.

Mr. Woodson Dobgood was a multidimensional, intelligent man who had retired from State Government and was acutely aware of the violations that were being perpetrated against Redhawk. He boldly stepped forth to the podium to voice his concerns about the Coterie's negative actions toward one of its dedicated, efficient public servants—Redhawk. He told the Coterie that Redhawk's integrity was above reproach, indicating that he had followed her career as DAA Director the entire length of her service to Kinder County. He described her as being unbelievably resourceful and above all dedicated to serving the people of Kinder County with compassion and vision.

Mr. Dobgood told the Coterie that he recognized the fact that they had a tremendous responsibility, but it was not larger than life. It wasn't larg- er than being fair, respectful and truthful about the manner in which services were delivered and people were treated—especially the employees—the foot soldiers who actually carried out the business for which the Coterie itself was responsible.

Mr. Dobgood reminded the Coterie that Redhawk's family had inhabited Kinder County long before the current Coterie's generation was born. Which meant that her family had been working and paying taxes in Kinder County before any of them. He told Cleopatra and the Coterie that Redhawk's credentials were greater than anyone in the room, and she used her knowledge and skills positively to serve her fellowman. She did it quietly and gracefully, for she was in no way boisterous or boastful.

Mr. Dobgood reminded the Coterie that all of the qualities Redhawk used to be successful in the workplace had been skillfully passed on to the DAA staff through Redhawk's teaching and guidance. With all of her great leadership qualities, he reminded them that Redhawk went home quietly, for unknown reasons, at Cleopatra's and the Coterie's insistence. He stated that the request was a cold and terrible act and it was only an attempt to discredit Redhawk and lay the groundwork for dismissal or a forced retirement.

But he assured the vitriolic Coterie that it was not going to happen.

So, Mr. Dobgood, as did all other concerned citizens in the room, wanted to know what game the Coterie was playing with the life of a fellow human being since they had surreptitiously schemed to concoct a cockamamie story to arouse public suspicion of Redhawk's honesty and integrity. Finally, Mr. Dobgood stated that in the end, Kinder County citizens won't have to judge what the Coterie has done. A higher power will do the honors.

The last speaker at the public forum was Mrs. Serena Walton. In Kinder County the name Serena Walton is synonymous with "Grand Lady." She was so highly respected in Kinder County that most residents never felt anything for her but the deepest admiration. Mrs. Walton, born and reared in Kinder County, had retired from the Federal Government and moved back to her roots. Having had assignments that took her all over the world, she recognized gross violations of federal laws relative to employee harassment and discrimination, as well as Hatch Act violations. And it appeared to Mrs. Walton that the Coterie was in violation of all three of the areas mentioned in terms of maltreatment of Redhawk.

Mrs. Walton stated to the Coterie that she

wasn't even aware of the ridiculous situation they had gotten themselves into until she read about it in the newspaper. She, too, questioned the Coterie's rea- son for having taken the drastic measure of placing an employee on *investigatory leave* with no explanation of what they were investigating. She wondered about the legality of the Coterie's action in this situation they had created of their own volition without justification.

Speaking of Redhawk, Mrs. Walton stated, she does what she is asked to do. She does what she is required to do. She serves Kinder County's needy population within the bounds of all regulations, statutes, and laws. "So what is your problem?" she asked the Coterie. Mrs. Walton told the Coterie that she was going to pray for truth and justice. And she wanted the Coterie to know that Kinder County supporters of Redhawk were going to stick with Redhawk come "*hell or high water!*"

ONGOING SAGA

Following the public forum and a few weeks of more digging for dirt, and being unable to find any, Cleopatra sent Redhawk a letter that stated in essence that Redhawk's job performance had been unsatisfactory. That a year and a half prior, Redhawk had been issued a *written warning* for *unsatisfactory performance of duties and unacceptable personal conduct.* Are you kidding me? Redhawk displaying unacceptable personal conduct? On which planet? Cleopatra had one heck of an imagination! But this accusation was stretching it too far! Of what was Redhawk being accused?

According to Cleopatra, Redhawk had failed to assure reimbursement for Medical Transportation was accurate. *A bold-faced lie!* Cleopatra didn't even understand the Medical Transportation reimbursement process! She had only been in her new bully position for six months and during that time she had never gone to the DAA agency to try and gain an understanding of the programs and processes. On a daily basis she instead stood sanctimoniously on the other side of the street dreaming and scheming more machinations to stir up more trouble for Redhawk and the DAA.

Cleopatra also falsely accused Redhawk of approving requests for DAA staff reimbursement prior to an activity—yet she could never explain nor give a rationale for making such ridiculous accusations. She went on to say that Redhawk conducted personnel functions contrary to Kinder County's Personnel Policies—policies that had not been updated in seven or eight years. Policies that Redhawk had correctly applied all those years and throughout her career as DAA Director. If Cleopatra and May Rhinestone had changed the policies, they had failed to notify Redhawk and other department keepers, and they surely had not presented any written changes in policies. And as far as Redhawk was concerned, if it wasn't written, and had not been communicated orally, then she was not in a position to make changes willy-nilly.

Cleopatra and May Rhinestone accused Redhawk of submitting recommendations to hire a candidate for employment when the position had never been posted to allow any other qualified candidates to apply. That was another lie and one that could be easily proven as a lie. But no one was listening because no one in authority really cared about the maltreatment Redhawk was receiving. All the Coterie wanted was for Redhawk to disappear. It didn't matter what Cleopatra did to make it happen. They just wanted the job done!

CONFERENCE

So, Redhawk shared with her attorney, Ellerby Watts, all of the inequities that were being perpetrated upon her. Redhawk had already shared her dilemma with Ray Rivers, the County Keeper, and this was the County Keeper's response during their conference: *Ray Rivers stated that he was going to speak to Cleopatra and tell her she needed to get to know more about the DAA agency and more about Redhawk before making any inaccurate accusations. He stated he was going to tell Cleopatra that we needed to have an event wherein the two departments (Waste and DAA) and respective staff could become better acquainted. He asked Redhawk if that would be OK with her. Of course, Redhawk had no objections to such a gesture. Redhawk's objection was to having a letter of warning in her personnel* file. But Ray Rivers, even though he agreed with Redhawk face-to-face, was afraid to ask Cleopatra to remove the letter, even though, organizationally, he was Cleopatra's boss and should not have been reluctant to offer her advice or give her instructions. In actuality, Cleopatra was his boss—she was everybody's boss because Servicious allowed her to have her way about everything.

Rivers had also made some comments to the media about internal problems within Kinder County Government's individual departments following an anonymous negative report about mistreatment of employees in Kinder County Government. He took the opportunity during the conference with Redhawk to say that his comments had not been directed toward Redhawk and the Department of Alliance Activity. He stated that all departments had a problem with turning to the media for help. Redhawk told Ray Rivers that no one really knew who had been contacting the media about the problems within Kinder County local government. While the Cote- rie and Cleopatra pointed their fingers toward DAA staff, it could have been disgruntled clients, spouses of staff, or genuinely concerned citizens. Redhawk told the County Keeper that she did not appreciate Cleopatra's implication that Redhawk was responsible for it. It appeared that anything and everything

that happened within local government to the Cote-
rie's disliking, the blame was placed on Redhawk.

Redhawk explained to Ray Rivers that Kinder County's so-called merger of the two departments left a lot to be desired because (a) there had never been a transition team formed; (b) no manual instructions or changes had been produced for the Department of Alliance Activity to follow; (c) there had never been a joint meeting of the two departments (Waste and DAA) to gain a better understanding of expecta- tions for working together; and (d) there had only been orders barked by Cleopatra with many of her requests being outside the purview of DAA policies because she neither knew nor understood what the policies were. And even if she had stepped across the street to try and learn anything about the agency's operation, there wasn't a chance that she could have learned all she needed to know within a six-month period.

Ray Rivers stated he was going to speak to Cleopatra about how disrespectful she had been to Redhawk and the DAA staff, and about the manner in which she failed to communicate with a department over which she had been given supervisory authority. He reiterated that Cleopatra did not understand the administration of DAA programs nor any of Redhawk's and the staff's responsibilities.   Duh?

Yet he said, "We are going to work this out."

Redhawk never heard another word from him nor did she ever receive any follow-up on his plans for smoothing things over. However, Redhawk believed Ray Rivers must have broached the subject with the Coterie and Cleopatra because a few months later she heard and observed Ray Rivers cleaning out his office and getting out of town.

The same issues and facts that were shared with Ray Rivers were also shared with Redhawk's attorney, Ellerby Watts. Additionally, Redhawk explained the impetus for the whole disciplinary fiasco. It seemed that while Redhawk was attending a state-wide DAA Directors' meeting in Atlantic City a week earlier, someone notified WMAT-TV7 that DAA staff had been working overtime for months and had never been compensated for all those hours. When the news was reported, the newly appointed Waste Director for Kinder County taunted DAA staff, and spoke to some of them in a threatening manner because she was angry about the media story. Ultimately, she directed her anger toward Redhawk in the form of the written warning (over something that Redhawk was not a party to and knew nothing about) that was the subject of the discussion.

Redhawk explained to her attorney, Ellerby

Watts, that Cleopatra had tried to antagonize her since the day her appointment as Waste Director was announced. Redhawk believed what really bothered Cleopatra more than anything else was that Cleopatra held a Master's of Public Administration degree while Redhawk was a Doctor of Public Administration. Redhawk offered that she had graciously accepted the Coterie's unfair appointment of the lesser qualified Cleopatra over her because it wasn't the first time she had been discriminated against, and with so much experience in that area, she knew how to handle it. Redhawk stated she was going to continue her excellent job performance and let them continue to think that they were almighty. What bothered Redhawk most was the bold and disrespectful actions taken against her and the DAA staff was continuing to get progressively worse. Redhawk asked Mr. Watts if he would write a letter to the Chairman of the Coterie, Ray Rivers and Kinder County's Analyst, Etum Sword, requesting removal of the written warning from her personnel file, and cessation of the harassment.

Would you believe that the Coterie, Ray Rivers, and Etum Sword, the County Analyst never ever did, even until this very time, respond to Attorney Watts? They never said "No, we are not going to do it!" They simply treated Mr. Watts and Redhawk as if they didn't even exist.

Getting back to Cleopatra's letter that was full of other similar gunk of her own creation due to her limited knowledge of the DAA, correspondence from the State of Xenolina, and lack of understand- ing overall, her bottom line and final warped decision was to demote Redhawk to Case Agent III without a shred of evidence to justify her actions. Imagine hav- ing been demoted by someone who didn't even un- derstand what she was supposedly handling? It was a pathetic situation. But one that Redhawk would cir- cumvent because it was all wrong. Cleopatra was so bent on covering up the fact that she had misled the Coterie and Servicious on numerous occasions in her effort to discredit Redhawk that in the final analysis, she was a desperate woman. She had to take extreme measures to get rid of Redhawk (because she had observed following numerous attempts to get rid of her that Redhawk was not going to leave voluntarily, even after Cleopatra had created a hostile work envi- ronment) in order to conceal the fact that she didn't know, or wasn't knowledgeable about DAA matters after having been in the position of Waste Director for two whole years. So, when it all boiled down to the fact that there had been searches of records for who knows how long to dig for some dirt in Red- hawk's past, nothing had been found (because there was nothing to be found), she had to save face with the Coterie, Servicious, and the public somehow. So,

Cleopatra asked herself, "Should I give Redhawk the death sentence (fire her)? Or should I give her life in prison (an unwarranted demotion, and subsequent humiliation to the lowest level)?"

In the end, Cleopatra's final decision amounted to *"life in prison."* Because she felt that a demotion would humiliate Redhawk into quitting (would inflict the ultimate mortification) and that would make it easy for her to justify the injustices she had dumped on Redhawk . Cleopatra and the *"powers-that-be"* had decided that they would show Redhawk, once and for all, who had the final say—right or wrong! They would show her that they *do what they want to do, whenever they want to do it, to whomever they want to, wherever they want to.* They were going to show Redhawk who was boss, and in doing so, show all Kinder County employees and citizens that they should let their actions with Redhawk be a warning to them that if the Coterie says employees have done wrong, whether it is true or not, the employees had better not dispute the almighty Coterie, or they, too, will be punished in a manner such that they would wish they had not spoken up to defend themselves against the treachery perpetrated by the Coterie.

WRONG DECISION

And they announced that Redhawk had been demoted from the position she had held and mastered for 30 years to case-agent III. Not case-agent IV; not supervisor; but case-agent III. If Cleopatra thought that Redhawk could be paled into insignificance by her evil actions, she was sadly mistaken. Who did Cleopatra think she was that she could make Redhawk feel ignominious? What a joke! The Coterie of Kinder County really knew how to show its board lacked intelligence, but instead was full of resentment and hatred for one particular loyal employee. If their plan was to engender vituperative threats from Redhawk, their plan failed miserably. Redhawk remained cool. When people discover that you won't allow them to push you around, they will pretend to look upon you favorably—all the while despising you.

Redhawk was sensitive enough to read the Coterie's actions and know the real deal. For it had been stated quite clearly by a member of the Coterie on numerous occasions, "We have to do something about Redhawk!" The listeners knew it meant that they wanted to be rid of Redhawk as Director of Alliance Activity. And what Coterie members did not realize was that the very people they were kvetching to were passing the word to Redhawk. In the midst of it all, Redhawk continued to embrace hope and reject fear, even though she knew she was being pursued by a ruthless, heartless, paid (by the Coterie) assassin.

A few years earlier the Coterie, with Cleopatra as the lead, had pulled a similar stunt on several nurses, Jill Carmichael and Hilda Litchfield, who were employed at the Waste Department. Both nurses were outstanding public servants. Terminating their employment without any justifiable reasons was not only a shock to them, but everyone who knew what had happened was flabbergasted. It did not seem possible that Cleopatra could dismiss staff without cause and move on as if she had committed no infraction, shown no concern over the fact that she had devastated, not only two staff members, but two families by suddenly, unexpectedly decreasing their household income, possibly by 50 percent. But Cleopatra, being devoid of some emotions, was blinded to the havoc she   had wreaked, and the emotional pain she had caused.

The magnitude of the devastation to the nurses' families when their employment was wrongful- ly terminated was so intense that one of the nurses committed suicide. One would think that Cleopatra would have cooled her jets after having caused such a tragedy, but she didn't. If anything, she was so fascinated by her imaginary power to destroy that she escalated her acerbic actions. She actually appeared triumphant. But fortunately, in the episode involving the two nurses, one of them, Jill Carmichael, had the wherewithal to sue Cleopatra and the Coterie. Mrs. Carmichael won the lawsuit. More Kinder County employees should stand up for themselves and fight the Coterie's furtive actions.

Often people do not understand the global and holistic ramifications of their dirty deeds—and if they do understand, they don't really care. Do people really think they can perpetrate drastic negative actions for no valid reason at all, against others in the 21st century with no consequences? It was incomprehensible that such a mindset subsisted. It is a scientific fact that for every action there is an equal and opposite reaction, and this concept applies in a broad array of venues and situations, physical as well as psychological.

Redhawk was often described as a workaholic. So to scheme to remove her from the work force could have been detrimental for her had she not had other skills and talents to keep her steadily employed and otherwise occupied. It takes time to get over the shock of being ordered, for no reason of any validity, from an environment where you have served dutifully, faithfully, professionally, masterfully and compassionately for more than 30 years.

Redhawk knew she had to take some action to make it clear to the Coterie and help them understand the impact of how severe emotional distress takes a toll on one's peace of mind and motivates them to take action—positive or negative. It's the revenge motive. People who live in glass houses should not throw stones. So, appropriate action in this case was to point out to the Coterie some of the many destruc- tive, unwarranted actions the Coterie itself had tak- en over the years to destroy individuals and organizations, and how as guardians of public trust, it had wasted taxpayers' dollars and actually abused public trust.

A good example is when the 2012 election was held, the people of Kinder County voted and approved a school bond referendum for the purpose of renovating some older school buildings and, where necessary, constructing new buildings. It was a complete shock to Servicious when the bond referendum passed, as it was not his intent to improve Kinder County Schools. His concentration was on his hidden agenda that was incongruent with school improvement.

When the Kinder County School Board presented the school-improvement plan to Servicious and the Coterie, Servicious balked on it. He repeatedly gave excuses for not releasing funds to move the Board of Education's plan forward. The frustration with Servicious' antics began to take a toll on members of the Board of Education to the point that the Chairman resigned his position and vacated the Board completely. This must have been painful for him because he had devoted untold numbers of hours in pursuit of an improved school system for Kinder County.

Today, Servicious still refuses to release the necessary funds for the school-improvement project. These are funds that the citizens, by the mere fact of approving the School Bond Referendum, designat- ed to be used as the Board of Education and Super- intendent of Schools, in their expert opinions, saw fit. So, citizens wanted to know, and are still asking, what happened to the school bonds? Why weren't the funds being released? As long as Servicious remains at the top, he will continue to be full of snide remarks and crass quips, and harbor no compunction about lying to the citizens of Kinder County.

Perhaps the Coterie is so comfortable with its power that it is shrouded in a cloud that gives them a feeling of being untouchable, because having violated federal rules and state regulations through discriminatory practices over the years, nothing has been done to bring to a halt their nefarious actions.

REDHAWK

Redhawk could be miserable, letting the Coterie have control of her emotions and life, or she could do something constructive, keeping her emotions in check and moving forward with her life—good as it had always been—or remain stuck in a state of self-pity. Redhawk had always been one to face forward, and this present situation was not going to change that fact. So move on she did. Somewhere she had read that where injustice prevails in a hamlet, city, country, our homes and even the church and we said or did nothing about it, the evil would not only continue, but grow larger and more intense.

At some point in time during a discriminatory episode, a decision has to be made as to whether or not it is worth continuing to work in the midst of people who behave the way the Coterie of Kinder County did in the work force. More specifically, whether or not the benefits and rewards are worth the pain, agony, and distress caused by such heartless, egomaniacal, mean-spirited individuals. So for months Redhawk pondered the question of "Should I stay or should I go?" And the overwhelming weight came down on the side of *"leave those people (troubles) behind!"* After all, she was planning to retire in the year 2017, so what would be lost by leaving a year earlier? What would be gained by staying? Redhawk's ability to cope with the multitude of problems that came with the territory of her job was fortified by the fact that she had a supportive DAA Board and DAA Management Team and staff that were comprised of highly intelligent members.

BOARD OF THE DEPARTMENT OF ALLIANCE ACTIVITY (DAA)

Until the final coup was taken by the Coterie to destroy the DAA Board, the Board had been a mainstay for the people of Kinder County who utilized DAA services. Not only for clients, the Board was a source of strength for DAA staff and the DAA Director. Over the years, visionaries on the DAA Board suggested many useful ideas that were initiated on behalf of disadvantaged Kinder County citizens.

In order to gain an idea of the character and skills of the DAA Board, some members are herein described. There was at one time a mighty fine southern gentleman, Jim McIntosh, who served two terms as Chairman of the Board. Married to his gracious lady for many years, and having a family of professionals, several of whom were employed at a DAA agency   in a neighboring county, he held a wealth of knowledge of DAA rules and regulations. Moreover, he was well liked and highly respected throughout Kinder County and the entire region. Mr. McIntosh was a compassionate soul who was deeply concerned about the care and well-being of DAA clients. Having a value system that was established through his Christian upbringing, he lived by the Golden Rule and fought for human rights. Mr. Jim, as he was affectionately known, never missed a Board meeting, and he always took a special interest in staff and morale at the DAA. He readily participated in all agency morale boosters arranged for staff from *Awards Night* celebrations to *Christmas Breakfasts.* Any special programs and/or events arranged for clients, their families and foster families and children, you could count on Mr. Jim being there to lend support. The DAA director and staff described him as *one-in-a-million* in terms of being a citizen dedicated to voluntary public service. Mr. Jim was jovial, witty, and fun to be around. He offered numerous ideas for improving programs and services offered by the Department of Alliance Activity.

Mrs. Victoria Crystal was one of the educa-tors on the DAA Board. Having taught elementary and middle school in Kinder County, she had a long history with a majority of Kinder County families because she had seen so many of their children grow up, finish college, get married, and start families of their own—some of whom now utilized services at the Department of Alliance Activity. In this regard she, too, was a tremendous asset to the DAA Board because she had firsthand background knowledge on many of the families served. As an educator, Mrs. Crystal was among the best of the best. She had been awarded the esteemed honor of *Teacher of the Year* on more than one occasion. As a community volunteer, she not only served on the DAA Board, but she volunteered at the Kinder County Hospital, located in the town of Marigold, as well as provided *free* tutoring service at the local high school. Even though she was retired, Mrs. Crystal was known for being highly energetic and gifted with great intelligence.

The DAA Board had a number of representatives from the faith community during Redhawk's tenure. One of the most memorable being the Rev. Hal Crown. Rev. Crown hailed from the westernmost corner of Kinder County and ebulliently represented his area, as well as citizens throughout the county, with a sense of peace and reverence. He was admired and respected by the people of Kinder County. In his leisure time, little that there was, he strummed a mean guitar, and was often found swinging on his front porch serenading his lovely wife. Out of those periods of relaxation flowed some masterful ideas for improving service to DAA clients. Being a servant of the Lord, Rev. Crown held a deep sense of compassion for serving God's people.

No organization can maximize its human resources and their talents without input from great analysts. The DAA Board was fortunate to have the service and skills of Dee Brighton. Mrs. Brighton would assess any problems presented before the Board, analyze it, weighing the pros and cons and make a recommendation for the DAA Director to follow. Having a kaleidoscope of talents supporting and advising the DAA Director lent credence to her success in managing a complex agency. To think that Cleopatra and the Coterie abolished an entity known to provide intelligence for serving low-income and disadvantaged citizens is incomprehensible. Yet they did it in Kinder County. They did it knowing that the Coterie itself was not going to contribute to the agency's success because they detested the DAA and all that it represents. Mrs. Brighton was not deterred by this lack of insight on the part of the Coterie. In an unofficial capacity, she continued to support the DAA as strongly as she had before the big breakup.

The law enforcement arm of government representing the community also had a representative serving on the DAA Board. It was represented by Capt. Susie Desiree, who dealt with many DAA clients in a judicial aspect. Highly respected by her colleagues on the DAA Board, the DAA Director and staff, as well as clients served by the agency, Capt. Desiree added prominence to the Board, and subsequently the Department of Alliance Activity. Capt. Desiree was highly visible in the community—spreading her youthful energy to all four corners of Kinder County. She could be seen at festivals, participating in a variety of school activities, including sports, and she volunteered her services with community youths at various churches. Being well known, Capt. Desiree was the perfect candidate for adding luster and spice to the DAA Board.

In earlier times in previous years, the Coterie felt it was necessary to have its own representation on the DAA Board. During the time when the Cote- rie was comprised of members who cared about all people of Kinder County, Fred Wrenchbark, a Colonel and Chairman of the Coterie, served on the DAA Board. There was never a problem brought beforethe DAA Board that the Colonel didn't set out to find appropriate resources for resolving whatever the problem happened to be. He was also one who—as the expression goes—put his money where his mouth is. He would generously donate to foster children and families, and later on when new cold-hearted members joined the Coterie, he would support the agency and staff when the Coterie as a body refused to do so.

One of the all-time staunchest supporters of the DAA agency was Derek Powers. He was young, handsome, blond, blue-eyed, and tanned from do- ing farm work. He had a camaraderie with farmers throughout Kinder County that gave him a unique information network, as farmers tend to know more about everything and everybody than the general Kinder County population. Additionally, Derek Pow- ers and his family owned a store that served as the hub, or Grand Central, if you will, of the section of the county from which he hailed. He was known for his easygoing mannerism and his contemplative pos- ture on issues of importance impacting the citizens of Kinder County. When he spoke, you can believe everyone listened because before giving a response to any question or commenting on any matter or is- sue; he is known to have given serious thought to both sides of the matter at hand. For these and other rea- sons, he was an Internet of information for the DAA Department. He was often the only member of the old guard to stand up for the Department of Alliance Activity. The fact that he served in the dual capaci- ty of Coterie member and DAA Board member was a blessing for the people of Kinder County, and es- pecially for Redhawk and staff who administered the agency's programs.

A few years later, Dave Intel replaced Der- ek Powers as the DAA Board member representing that particular area of the county. The tall, dark, and handsome Dave Intel was one who was extreme- ly knowledgeable about Kinder County Government through his governmental contacts at the State Super Power because he was an employee of Xenolina and had previously worked for years at a DAA agency. He was a smorgasbord of great suggestions for serving the people of Kinder County. As a public servant, he was aware of the many unmet needs and difficulties encountered when efforts are put forth to garner the necessary resources for properly addressing those needs.

Imagine this wide variety of talents and skills being ignored by a Coterie Board who had none of these specifics in their narrow governmental reper- toire.

It would be an injustice to omit two very fine educators that represented the same area of Kind- er County, albeit during different terms on the DAA Board. They were not only knowledgeable and wise, they were also compassionate, energetic, and highly enthusiastic about the opportunity to serve Kinder County citizens in the capacity of DAA Board members. Their connections in the education milieu made them invaluable members to parents and children served by the Department of Alliance Activity. These ladies, Amelia Jones and Antoinette Kennedy, were open to parental consults and served as liaisons between the Board of Education, and the DAA, providing a unique link to the community. There was not a single educator serving on the Coterie at the time—because they had driven Sunshine from the group and he was highly educated—and consequently, the Coterie, due to its lack of understanding, was always at loggerheads with members of the Board of Education, and often with the DAA Board as well.

One of two firehorses on the DAA Board, Bill Guardsman, was well-known for his community and political activism. He represented the north-easternmost section of Kinder County and never shied away from a fight to bring the best services Kinder County had to offer to his area. He fought to get county water, and won. He fought to get other county facilities in his area, and won. And he fought for the disadvantaged and underprivileged citizens throughout Kinder County. It was not unusual to find him at a Coterie meeting speaking on behalf of a citizens' group or community, for the purpose of improving the quality of life in a populous area or some remote location in Kinder County. DAA clients who needed a   spokesman looked to Mr. Guardsman to assist them in making a point or championing a cause. He always found a way to make himself available. So it was advantageous having him serving on the DAA Board because the Coterie knew he was going to hold steadfastly to his position on agency issues of importance, whatever they happened to be.

While there was a drove of other members of the DAA Board shoring up its strength, the most colorful, dynamic, empathetic, and resourceful member was the gentleman holding the chairmanship at the time the Coterie abolished or disbanded the DAA Board, Mr. Francis Perry. Mr. Perry was a Federal Government retiree. His knowledge of governmental administration was outstanding, being factually based due to many years of training during his tenure as a governmental agent. While he held a broad base of understanding in a variety of areas, he was extremely astute in discriminatory law practice. Being of Latino descent, he had not only witnessed discrimination throughout his life, he had also experienced it. Therefore, he would go to great lengths to see that DAA clients received fair and equal treatment. He abhorred the unequal treatment that the DAA Director and staff received from the Coterie. When he would make attempts to speak to Coterie members about their disparaging actions, Coterie members would make themselves unavailable. Sometimes they would give him an appointment, but would fail to show up at the appointed time. Sometimes if he were fortunate enough to catch them in their office, the Coterie would ease out the back door—always treating him indifferently as if he were a non-person, and that any issue he wanted to present or discuss was insignificant or inconsequential.

Mr. Perry was a real *"go-getter."* He secured contracts with large food-chain stores to collect food for needy clients. On a weekly basis stores would give the DAA agency fruits, vegetables, frozen entrees, canned goods, including canned meat, to feed families who for various reasons could not afford sufficient meals for their families DAA staff would go above and beyond the bounds of a mere position description to ensure families received these foods. However, when the Coterie decided to abolish the DAA Board, Mr. Perry received a letter from Cleopatra informing him that he could no longer arrange for food to be brought to the DAA agency to be given to clients. This is just another example of the meanness, callousness, and insensitivity of the Coterie. Clearly, it indicates the Coterie's disdain for poor people. It's no wonder the Coterie devised a plan to abolish the DAA Board. The DAA Board represented great strength for the   DAA

Director, staff, and especially DAA clients. Strength that the Coterie loathed.

THE DAA MANAGEMENT TEAM

The DAA Management Team served as an arm of the DAA Director and provided the structural foundation of day-to-day operations and administration of agency programs. The strength of this team was fortified by the longevity, knowledge, and experience of its members. There were 14 representatives covering the subdivisions of the two main agency divisions. Collectively, the team added 315 years of training and experience to the DAA. That was a force to be reckoned with. Teamwork was the reason why the Kinder County DAA agency always scored 100 percent in most program areas the majority of the time agency reviews were held. Of course, there were a few times when the agency's scores ranged from 90 percent to 98 percent accuracy but, for the most part, the citizens of Kinder County were assured that DAA   work was both accurately and efficiently completed under Redhawk's administration and leadership, and assurance was also provided that overall, clients were served timely and accurately.

The DAA Management Team went above and beyond the call of duty to ensure timely and quali- ty service within the bounds of the rules of law and guidelines within which the agency operated.

The two major divisions under the agency's umbrella were Economic Services and Family, Adult and Children Services. The Director of Economic Services, Paisley Ward, sported more than 30 years of experience, with the training to support the mountain of knowledge she had acquired over the years.

Paisley Ward, a beautiful young country girl, was surrounded by all brothers in a loving family household. Being the only girl, she was a serious tomboy. She was a bright girl as could be attested by her grades in school where she remained on the "A" Honor Roll for the entire 12 years she attended. In college she also excelled, and true to her tomboy mindset, she majored in Criminal Justice.

Paisley brought her suspicions of people trying to cheat the system, learned while studying criminal justice, with her when she joined the Department of Alliance Activity. She first worked as a Social Worker before she began training in Economic programs where she quickly escalated to the position of supervisor following the retirement of one staff who had supervised Economic Services for many years.

Paisley Ward was known for her high-energy level—some even called her hyperactive—that enabled her to work many long hours beyond the 40-hour work week. On any given evening after hours she could be found at her desk plowing through mounds of paperwork. Over the years, she earned the moniker *eagle eye*. She was firm in her belief that staff needed to be checked constantly on their comprehension of rules and regulations, and consequently spent an enormous number of hours reviewing their work and conducting second-party reviews of the supervisors for whom she was responsible. All of this checking and Ms. Ward's ideals for the agency were obvious at review time. As a result of her relentlessness, for years the subdivisions under her supervision earned 100 percent accuracy of records that were examined.

Even though Redhawk listened patiently whenever staff complained that they were being driven too hard by Ms. Ward, Redhawk always assured staff that she was proud of their dedicated service and that they really were not under threat of job loss. After all, they were giving Kinder County citizens 110 percent of their professional services. Redhawk also assured Ms. Ward that she was doing an outstanding job of ensuring that client needs were being met. And that was always the bottom line and ultimately the only acceptable outcome.

Ms. Ward's counterpart on the Family, Adult and Children Services Division was Ms. Jordan West. Growing up and all through life, Jordan had also been an honor student, excelling in high school, undergrad, and graduate school. Like Paisley, Jordan too, grew up in a household surrounded by brothers. But unlike Paisley, Jordan was not a tomboy. Jordan West was the true depiction of a lady. She was graceful, statuesque, and charming. She had a certain magnetism about her to which staff under her supervision were drawn. Because of this quality, Ms. West was able to get staff to produce its optimal performance of essential functions simply by pointing out what needed to be done.

Ms. West's tenure at the DAA was split because Ms. West was adventuresome. At one time during her career, Ms. West left the Kinder County DAA to serve as program manager in an adjoining county. However, after several years in that area, Jordan West realized that the Kinder County Department of Alliance Activity under Redhawk's leadership was where she wanted to be. So, Jordan returned, was welcomed, and resumed her supervisory role in Kinder County. Redhawk was elated to have the talent, skills, and experience of Jordan return to Kinder County.

Being the tremendous supervisor that she was, monitoring reports on Kinder County DAA from the State of Xenolina were always good, very good, and excellent. Great teamwork is a force that drives any organization to successful heights. Redhawk prided herself in taking all the necessary steps and actions to ensure that the Kinder County DAA Management Team was a machine that was built of the finest individual parts and was well oiled. Jordan West was one of those parts. As a leader, Redhawk put forth a colossal effort to always be present with the team and committed to whatever tasks confronted the DAA Management Team.

The DAA Management Team met regularly on a monthly basis. Exceptions occurred whenever there were special circumstances that warranted meeting more frequently. All members always appeared genuinely interested and concerned about the success of the agency—especially morale of staff and service to clients. In that regard, the team was to a large degree, family oriented.

The DAA Management Team was a magnificent

piece of work in terms of its organizational behavior toward the agency as a global entity and a facilitator of services to the needy Kinder County population. It was fine tuned. It was not broken. It did not need to be fixed. So what was Cleopatra's and the Cote- rie's problem with the way the agency was operating? Simple! It was the driver of the machine, Redhawk!

Of all the members of the DAA Management Team, June Jaxon could be considered the mainstay. Ms. Jaxon held a degree in Business Administration and served as accountant for the Department of Alliance Activity. She was a quiet storm in terms of maximizing numbers and techniques to get the best returns on the dollar for Kinder County. She worked quietly and diligently. Redhawk considered JJ, as she affectionately referred to Ms. Jaxon, as her right arm. Because no matter what criticisms, big or small, Redhawk and the agency received, as long as the accounting was accurate, all those other criticisms paled. And the accounting was always accurate because of the knowledge and skills of Ms. June Jaxon.

June Jaxon was a true Christian lady. She always extended herself to support others—not simply when she was called upon, but she volunteered her talent and skills at church and in the community, as well as in situations at work where her skills were needed outside of the bounds of her position description. June Jaxon was honorable and trustworthy, and Redhawk would have trusted June with her life if she had to. June is one of the reasons Redhawk could sleep so well at night even though she was responsible for managing and leading one of the largest agencies in Kinder County. June's trustworthiness was invaluable to Redhawk, so much so that June became godmother to Redhawk's only grandchild—a boy named Strafield.

June herself was a wife and mother of an only child. So, Redhawk knew that June understood the importance of having another trusted human being readily available to step forth and help an only child should it ever become necessary.

While Paisley Ward, Jordan West, and June Jaxon played key roles on the DAA Management Team, the other 11 members had roles of equal importance. And because of it, there was not a more successful management team in Kinder County.

DEPARTMENT OF ALLIANCE ACTIVITY STAFF

The DAA staff was always a great source of strength and motivation for Redhawk. Staff consisted of a patchwork of beautiful characters and personalities that, when melded collectively, created a team of unbeatable talents, DAA knowledge, and skills. They were all specialists in their assigned areas of benefits and service delivery. They were a tough bunch who didn't waste time fighting with the Devil, but instead expended their energies deciphering new rules and applying them accurately and appropriately to serve DAA clients.

They were a bridge over troubled waters for many families who were feeling a sense of desperation and hopelessness because they were faced with problems that overwhelmed them—often to the point of collapse.

They were earthquakes who could shake and break through convoluted rules and regulations that temporarily prevented clients from having their needs met.

They were fire and wind and rain and snow or whatever was needed at a given moment to perform the essential functions of their respective jobs.

They were the bright spot in a dark tunnel; ladders where there were holes out of which clients had to climb; spikes when facing mountains to be climbed; parachutes when client were hopelessly falling; scissors when there was red tape to cut through; flotation devices when clients felt they were drowning; water when clients were thirsty; and food when clients were hungry.

They were the last best hope for the destitute, the impoverished, or the low income who needed only temporary assistance until their lives and situations improved.

DAA staff wore the faces of love, kindness, compassion, consideration, thoughtfulness, and patience. All the while they were serving clients and the public in general; oftentimes they had problems of their own. But Redhawk and DAA staff were always supportive of one another—through births, illnesses, deaths, marriages, divorces, misunderstandings, and sadness. Through engagements and happiness, difficult communication and depression, dreams and visions, they held it together.

This was what made them a *"work force family."* This was how they survived the manipulative actions of Servicious and the Coterie and Cleopatra. Redhawk, the DAA Management Team, and DAA staff understood that there were untold numbers of uncertainties and sudden changes that disrupted their daily routines and plans. And knowing this, they were able to cope unabashedly with the Coterie's and Cleopatra's unfavorable treatment, and still carry out the duties they were hired to perform.

BOASTING

Cleopatra herself was telling people that she was going to do something that was going to "make a lot of black people mad." Two technicians specializing in Animal Husbandry, whom Cleopatra dearly despised, had been hired, for some reason, to work at the Animal Shelter. They overheard a conversa- tion wherein Cleopatra was bragging about how she was going to terminate Redhawk's employment. The two, being as kind as they are, felt they should get the word to Redhawk that Cleopatra was laughing and bragging about how she was going to bring about Redhawk's total ruination. The technicians had an ir- repressible urge to let Redhawk know what was forth- coming. And so did some male employees to whom Cleopatra had boasted that she had some *"old hacks"* over at the Department of Alliance Activity that   she was going to get rid of... starting at the top. And so, Redhawk was given the word from more than one source. It is amazing that the great effort Cleopatra and the Coterie put forth to undermine and shatter Redhawk's confidence, security, and well-being was a total failure. But Cleopatra felt with the destruction of the DAA Board, she could move forward with her pernicious plans.

Psychologists describe a person's tendency to be unemotional and able to detach himself or herself from conventional morality, and hence deceive and manipulate others as Machiavellianism. This description was a perfect fit for Cleopatra's tendencies to cause emotional harm to others, yet distance herself psychologically from the ruination she caused. When cunning tricks and duplicity are used in the workplace the Machiavellian phenomenon is operating. It is a personality characteristic that has been studied over the past 40 years that share features with manipulative leadership and moral bankruptcy. It is often utilized when a specific negative action needs to be camouflaged. Persons who employ this tactic have a *"cynical disregard for morality and focus on self-interest and personal gain."* Cleopatra was operating in this vein.

REDHAWK

The Coterie and its henchwoman Cleopatra failed to understand that Redhawk had a tough side. Maybe they were fooled by her lady-like mannerism. But if Redhawk's friends and family were to describe her as a particular make of automobile they would say that she is a Chevrolet. More specifically, they say that she is a dual Chevy truck with a 7.4 liter engine, series 3500, and 454 horsepower. They would give this true description because those who know her have often called her a "*workhorse,*" a "*workaholic,*" tough, durable with great fortitude and *true grit*. They often wondered why she continued to work at her age, but anyone who has ever owned a heavy Chevy knows that they are dependable, long-lasting, and ready and willing to take you wherever you need to go—from the fields to the store, school, job, party, church, wherever...the Chevy will hang with the best of the lot, *like a rock!*

In technical terms, Redhawk could be considered a *moderate conserver.* She would prefer that change be implemented gradually and incrementally. Unlike Cleopatra who makes drastic impulsive changes with little or no thought as to outcomes and the impact of her reckless decisions. Unlike Cleopatra, Redhawk understands that *leadership* is not the same as *authority,* and new situations must be approached in a deliberate and disciplined manner, taking caution to be diplomatic whenever and wherever necessary. This aspect of Redhawk's personality enabled and empowered her to lead by listening to both management and staff that, in part, accounts for the fact that she was able to work the last five years in the position of DAA Director in an extremely hostile work environment. The key value that undergirds Redhawk's philosophy is *"fairness."* Being fair enabled her to promote harmony in the workplace, be empathetic, boost morale, solve conflicts, and basically be a genuinely nice affiliative boss. With the advent of Cleopatra in the leadership role, all of those leadership qualities vanished because Cleopatra, as a leader, had none of them. From an organizational management perspective, instituting the merger of two functionally different co-equal departments, and elevating one over the other, violates all principles of sound management. The only reason for the Coterie having put Cleopatra, from a Health background, over Redhawk, with the Alliance Activity background, was for nefarious purposes.

CLEOPATRA

Cleopatra had morphed into a walking cliché of a tyrant. Her Hitler-like demeanor in the presence of DAA staff was terrifying for those who were faint in spirit and insecure in general. Cleopatra stalked through the agency periodically to keep staff reminded that she was in charge and if the mood hit her on any given day, she would send one of them packing. She created the ultimate hostile workplace environment. It did not matter how well a staff member was performing, or how demanding the essential functions of the position happened to be. If Cleopatra decided she didn't want someone around anymore, that was her only criterion for terminating someone's employment. And, sadly, whatever she did was fine with the Coterie.

Cleopatra enjoyed her role, as it was evidenced

by the ugly smirk that graced her face constantly. While Cleopatra was otherwise striking in appearance, that smirk, those dark eyes, and long dark hair make her appear sinister, witchy—and in fact she is a witch with a capital "B"! She is notoriously inconsistent in the manner with which she divvies out her hateful combustible fury.

EQUAL EMPLOYMENT OPPORTUNITY COMMISSION

It has been said that the Civil Rights Act of 1964 was a watershed moment for social justice in the nation. Under Title VII of the act, it became illegal for businesses to discriminate based on *"race, color, religion, gender, or national origin."* The Age Discrimination in Employment Act was ratified and instituted in 1967.

In recent times, the vote to grant all Xenoli- na counties the opportunity to merge several departments that here-to-fore had operated as separate entities under the Health and Human Services umbrella created a watershed moment for employees in those few counties that chose to implement that organizational structure. It diminished employee job security tremendously by removing State Personnel Protection, leaving employees protected only by Federal Equal Opportunity Employment Laws. These eight federal laws that protect employees—minimum wage, workplace safety, health coverage, social security, unemployment benefits, whistleblower protections, family leave, employment-based discrimination—were ignored by the Coterie anytime they decided to turn their heads on the law in a given situation. In Redhawk's case, Servicious, Cleopatra, and the Coterie wanted to strip Redhawk of at least five of the eight protections.

Redhawk explained everything that Shady Worm, County Keeper had failed to do to correct the injustices that Cleopatra and May Rhinestone had perpetrated against her with the Coterie's blessings. All three of those individuals were carrying out the Coterie's directives. So, the Coterie was central to the problem. Redhawk further elucidated why it was necessary at that point to retain legal counsel. She noted the unwarranted written warnings, false accusations, and intimidation and harassment tactics. She explained how at one meeting with the Coterie a request for equipment had been approved by the Coterie, with Cleopatra's approval as well. But somehow, within a week or two, Cleopatra found a way to twist the request into some infraction on Redhawk's part. *What a witch*!

Redhawk had to explain in detail some of the incidents that she felt were discriminatory—and she did! When all the information supplied to the EEOC had been assessed and analyzed, the EEOC ruled in Redhawk's favor and sent a letter granting Redhawk the right to sue Kinder County. At that point, the Coterie was ready to retract the erroneous, maliciously spiteful decisions they had made in an attempt to impugn Redhawk's integrity. All of this had been done to allow Cleopatra to save face, and to demote Redhawk or terminate her employment in order to take away her benefits. So, Redhawk's Attorney, Ellerby Watts, and the powerful law firm based in the capitol city of the State of Xenolina that had been retained by Kinder County to fight Redhawk, began negotiations. Months passed before a deal was struck that Redhawk found acceptable.

So, it appeared that Poindexter and her newfound cohorts had lost again. Poindexter really had thought that Redhawk was going to have to work under her supervision. However, one of the rewards to Poindexter for being such a creative liar was to promote her to the position of supervisor. Well now, that is surely a reward, but it is not what Poindexter was hoping for. Cleopatra didn't get it! Poindexter wanted to become DAA Director. All of that lying and the best she could get was supervisor? There just isn't any justice.

What Poindexter failed to understand was that Cleopatra didn't even like her kind. Cleopatra would never elevate Poindexter's status beyond supervisor. It pained Cleopatra to grant that small token. Poindexter didn't even realize that Cleopatra was on the verge of getting rid of her completely. Cleopatra was simply biding her time until the next budget had been constructed and a new DAA Director had been given the orders. Poindexter was going to be left out in the cold.

Cleopatra was not only receiving misinformation about Redhawk from Poindexter, there were other snakes in the grass lying in wait to strike Redhawk a deadly blow. In addition, there was one particular individual on the outside of Kinder County Government who had held a life-long fixation on Redhawk, and was trying every angle possible to destroy Redhawk. Her name was Chessa, who can best be described as a snarky character. However, with all her sarcasm about everything and everybody, she was still a counterfeit who thought she was smarter than most people in any room.

CHESSA

Chessa set out to weave the web of the century. She set her sights on the worldly goods inherited by Redhawk, and thought she had developed the perfect plan to destroy Redhawk's reputation. But just when Chessa thought she was at the point for a smooth execution of her plan that she had woven over a 30-some year period, she was knocked senseless, literally. All because she had deluded herself into thinking she was so smart. Actually, Chessa was wicked. Her hatred of Redhawk had festered since childhood and driven her to take some desperate measures in her quest to carry out her plan and take someone else's possessions. When her plan disintegrated, Chessa thought she could reconstruct it by ingratiating herself to Cleopatra.

Chessa, by all accounts in today's economy,

could be considered successful. However, Chessa wanted to be rich. She had always presented herself as aristocratic—heaven only knows how she formulated such an idea in that empty head of hers. But Chessa can't appreciate what she has and how far she has advanced in life because her sole concentration is on Redhawk, who she believes and who in fact has accomplished more and advanced farther. So, Chessa now planned to use Cleopatra to implement her plan to drag Redhawk through the mud. She saw Cleopatra as the perfect means to carry out this plan. And Cleopatra, being on a hunt for anyone who could help destroy Redhawk, fell for Chessa's lies hook, line, and sinker. Chessa and Cleopatra shared a common theme about Redhawk, "Let's destroy her!" And so their plan was developed.

Cleopatra and Chessa lived continuously in denial of reality. They knew the stories they told about Redhawk were lies born out of their jealousy and envy. Whether they realized it or not, they were surely paving a way to reach the mad house. There will always be someone greater and lesser than ourselves. We should be thankful for our own blessings and not burden ourselves coveting others.

Chessa was phony and deceptive. Always skinning and grinning with a facial expression she has mastered that she felt hid her ulterior motives when she was up to no good. In reality, she had nothing to laugh about because she had lost what she considered her major battle. So instead of her proud uppity stance, these days she wears the drooped shoulders of defeat. As of this point in time, Chessa knows from experience that if you look for trouble you will, in all likelihood, find it.

Chessa had a cadre of cohorts who assisted with conducting her research, such as it was. Mostly it was idle gossip and speculation. The team of them didn't do a good job of true discovery. Their method of gathering information consisted of calling on the telephone, posting on Facebook, and beating around the bush in their usual sly manner, never asking direct questions that were necessary to gain accurate answers. Therefore, they learned nothing and knew nothing. When in search of substance, one must boldly step forward and be direct and to the point. Chessa and her team had not reached that level of honesty, and probably never will. Acting desultorily has never produced useful information.

THE X.V.I.

And that is why when the implacable Cleopatra went to the Coterie with what she thought was deadly accurate destructive information against Redhawk, she felt she was making the ultimate power play that would surely be Redhawk's demise. As a matter of fact, Cleopatra was so sure of herself that she coerced the Coterie to secure the X.V.I. (Xeno- lina Valuation Inquirer) to investigate Redhawk. At the request of the Coterie, this agency will delve into the background of Kinder County employees, check- ing for misappropriation of funds, fraud, and other crimes that officials feel justify bringing in this technical assistance to work closely with the District Attorney, Sheriff, local police, or any law enforcement agency that has jurisdiction over what appears to be a problem that needs investigating. Much of the work is accomplished through computerized information on record where local government employee investigations are concerned.

Misuse of state property and funds is one of the areas where, if examined closely, the X.V.I. might find a cornucopia of violations in Kinder County. But Servicious was really not interested in the big picture of abuse within the county. He only sets his sights, erroneously judging of course, on people whom he despised for whatever reasons. Servicious would not only fabricate lies when it suited his purpose, he would withhold the truth in situations in order to have his way. If Servicious were really serious about his claim of always seeking transparency, when he sought the X.V.I.'s expertise to investigate Redhawk, he should also have had the X.V.I. audit Kinder County Government records to show the taxpaying citizens what happened to the $42 million that was once in the reserve fund (*rainy day or build-up fund*) that the Coterie at one time insisted Kinder County need- ed in order to remain financially solvent. The Cote- rie claimed never to have dipped into the funds for any reason. Wouldn't use any of those funds for the Kinder County Public Schools—or so it was asserted. Refused to dip into the reserve funds to grant sala- ry increases to Kinder County employees—leaving them to fall behind other workers in counties contiguous to, and surrounding, the Kinder County region. Yet the Coterie would give large sums to every little community, civic, and religious organization during the election years when Servicious was running for re-election. Where did that money come from? Certainly not from Servicious' campaign fund? Because who needed to give him donations when he was doling out contributions to entities that he felt he needed to win over in order to get their votes.

A number of Kinder County taxpayers questioned those actions and requested a State Audit over a six-year period, but nobody with the authority to do so bothered to inquire further or investigate. State Officials always said the request for a State Audit must come from the Kinder County Coterie. *Well, we thought the days of having the fox guard the henhouse had disappeared long ago when technology became the preferred mode for examining records.*

Since Servicious himself had insisted that there was *fraud* in Kinder County Government, perhaps he knew exactly where it was occurring. It certainly was not taking place at the Department of Alliance Activity where Redhawk was Director. Perhaps Servicious should be investigated by the X.V.I.

Everyone would agree that the X.V.I. should have been investigating some specific events in Kinder County Government, but it surely wasn't Redhawk. The X.V.I. should have been called upon to investigate the manner in which Servicious threatened Hunter Green, Political Director, with the loss of employment if Servicious lost the election, and promised Hunter plenty of fruit when Servicious was declared the winner. Hunter Green was a pleasant soul who loved to joke in a positive sense. His sense of humor could never be described as wicked because Hunter is a guy who only wants to have fun. He never, or so it seemed, used humor to denigrate anyone, or any group or entity. He had a magnetic personality. At the outset, Hunter appeared to be a care-free individual who was excited over having landed a job in Kinder County. He was always happy to assist and accommodate the voting population in a fair and impartial manner. Always when the election results were tallied, the people of Kinder County felt that Hunter Green had done a good job.

The X.V.I. should have been called upon to investigate what happened to the funds that were wasted supposedly spent on a building that was overpriced and has never been used to benefit the citizens of Kinder County. The building has set idle for five years with no floor (a dirt floor) with a $3 million price tag, plus an annual mortgage with payments of more than $275,000. Rumor has it that some of the money that was alleged to have been spent on the white elephant has actually been used to kickback funds to a few members of the Coterie. Let the X.V.I. investigate that!

Instead of allowing the big white-elephant building stand vacant, the Coterie could have had the wherewithal to make use of it. The building itself is in a prime location for people from all areas of Kind- er County to access without much difficulty. The entrance to it is on one major highway that is not more than three miles from the Interstate highway. You see, Kinder County has not had a county fair and the white-elephant building could provide a great ven- ue for county fair activities. There is space for displaying items usually found in booths at fairgrounds. And what's more, there would be a roof over artisans' products. But ideas of this nature are too far-fetched for the Coterie to grasp. Members of the Coterie don't think in terms of what's good for the people; they think in terms of *"self-aggrandizement."*

Space-wise, Kinder County offers an ideal setting for a county fair—moreso than neighboring counties. But, as has been emphasized, there is a short- age on initiative for bringing about fun and exciting activities for Kinder County citizens' enjoyment. As a matter of fact, there hasn't been a county fair in

Kinder County since the 1970s. One supposes that the emergence of various festivals is supposed to be an adequate replacement for a tradition that Coterie members might find so "*yesteryear.*" However, surrounding counties still capitalize on the revenue that fairs bring to their counties. Even citizens of Kinder County make the trek to those nearby counties to enjoy the fun and spice a county fair brings to a community.

The white elephant could also serve the public as a "*civic center.*" That's another facility missing from Kinder County. All surrounding counties have invested in civic centers or something akin to a civic center with accommodations ranging from sublime to extraordinary. They provide a venue where stars can entertain the public with awesome concerts and a variety of shows, to simple accommodations such as family reunions, weddings, and the like. Civic Centers also bring additional revenue to counties. The Coterie could have invested in a Civic Center to serve all Kinder County citizens, rather than waste $6 million—at least that's what they claim as the cost—renovating an old school that stands grossly under-utilized. What's worse, it serves only one side of Kinder County. At least the white elephant is centrally located in the county. If only the Coterie had the foresight and desire to put the white elephant to good use rather than let it stand idle as another bill for Kinder County citizens to pay, some of the void felt by the lack of revenue in Kinder County Government could be filled.

What about the need for buildings to house Kinder County employees? The Coterie has wasted taxpayer dollars on buildings that are not being used while employees sit in over-crowded offices. And the Coterie did not quit while they were behind. They went back to the well on an old dilapidated school building and invested another $6 million of taxpayers' funds. Does anyone actually believe that all of those funds were spent on renovations? Furthermore, the renovations were not substantial enough to have had a price tag that high. But what was even more ridiculous, there sat another expensive building that was not being fully utilized. As a matter of fact, the building was so under-utilized that the few staff who were sent there on occasion did not feel safe because they were so isolated.

The X.V.I. should have investigated how some of the material purchased to replace the floors in the Waste Department happened to have been used in   a remodeling project in a certain employee's home, and how the same ugly, retched-colored paint that was used in county buildings ended up on the walls of that employee's new den.

The X.V.I. should have investigated how Kinder County employees could hire or contract their spouses to complete county construction projects, a conflict of interest, but no disciplinary action or public humiliation with a much deserved investigation ever occurred. Everything was *hush-hush*! Real situations existed in Kinder County that warranted investigating, but those situations were overlooked because the people involved were a part of the Coterie's "*good old network*," so heads were turned and ears were deafened. But these same characters went out of their way to make up lies about other dedicated employees simply because they didn't want them around.

The X.V.I. should investigate whether or not a conflict of interest existed due to the fact that Servicious hired his wife. If anyone else even dreamed of hiring a spouse, Servicious would have gone ballistic! So, what special rules applied to nullify nepotism for some employees of Kinder County, but not others? Doesn't it violate federal laws to practice nepotism in any government, local or otherwise? Servicious should be made to answer the question since he says he believes in "*transparency,*" and he should have to make a payback for all the wrongs he has perpetrated.

REDHAWK

Thankfully, throughout the months that Redhawk was under the crossfire of Servicious, Cleopatra, and the Coterie, her fate was not in their hands as they had believed. Redhawk wondered why they were devoting so much time plotting and scheming against her rather than trying to secure a future for themselves. Did they feel she was some kind of threat to them? That team appeared to have a deadly interest in poisoning public opinion against Redhawk. What a waste of energy!

During this period of dubiety, Redhawk continued to hear from many friends and loved ones who reminded her that this was only a short chapter in her book of life. One friend said, *"You are a woman of many firsts, spanning four decades of service. Over the years, we have come to appreciate your awe-*

some spirit."

Throughout this ordeal, Redhawk had pondered whether or not she wanted to continue working in the midst of Servicious, Cleopatra, and the Coterie. It has been said that sometimes you have to choose between turning the page and closing the book. And in this case, Redhawk felt it was time to close the book. So on December 9th she sent a letter to the Coterie Chairman announcing her intent to retire effective January 31st. In the letter, she stated, *"After having served compassionately, diligently, faithfully and professionally, with excellence and profound dedication, I will retire in good standing from the position of Director of Alliance Activity for Kinder County effective January 31, 2016. I would like to thank the people of Kinder County for allowing me to faithfully serve them throughout my 33-year tenure. I would also like to thank the DAA staff, former and current, for its outstanding performance throughout the period of my service. Finally, I would like to thank the numerous state and county officials for the esprit de corps shown to Kinder County Department of Alliance Activity throughout the duration of my time as DAA Director for Kinder County."*

NEW DIRECTR OF ALLIANCE ACTIVITY

And the day finally came when Cleopatra found a person who could be trusted by her, Servicious, and the Coterie to join their kleptocratic ways without questions. And what do you know? It was not Miss Poindexter! When the announcement was made with great fanfare in the presence of DAA staff, Poindexter nearly collapsed from the shock. It was as if Cleopatra had hit her with a blast from a Taser. Poindexter broke out in a cold sweat so severe that her clothes looked as if someone had doused her with a victory spill. But Poindexter is not one to give up. Already she was beginning to use her feminine wiles to ingratiate herself upon the new DAA Director. The new man had better be careful because Poindexter already has him in her crosshairs.

REMINISCING AND REFLECTING

It was 11 days before Christmas—December 14th—when Redhawk sat quietly thinking about events of the past six months. She felt that those months had been unexpectedly, horribly different than anything she could have imagined in the closing chapter of her work life and tenure as DAA Director for Kinder County. Who would have thought that after 33 years of serving with a stellar reputation that she would have found herself suspended, without explanation from organizational superiors, and placed on *investigatory leave* that, by all accounts, created a cloud of suspicion that in the final analysis yielded no results that could ever be detrimental against her?

Redhawk was also thinking about how Kinder County citizens were still reeling from the nearly *40 percent tax increase* that had been forced on   them.

And it was being rumored that the Coterie was contemplating an additional *15 percent tax increase* in 2017. She was thinking that they must really need to rebuild the fund balance in a hurry. But citizens who had heard the rumor were wondering why rebuild the fund balance on the backs of taxpayers when the Coterie is the group that wasted taxpayer savings in the first place.

Industries are leaving Kinder County to locate elsewhere. On the western most side of Kinder County septic permits have been denied by Cleopatra, the Waste Department Director, in an effort to suppress growth in the county. The totalitarianism of the Coterie continues today, as yesterday, unchanged in nature and scope. With the Coterie in power, Kinder County citizens have been fed a diet of lies and alibis. When will the people wake up and take some corrective political action? How long will it take?

It is a pitiful public servant who *"leads by chasing rumors"* instead of totally concentrating on the work to be accomplished and the services to be rendered. A work-related issue should be appropriately addressed, not hidden secretively to grossly mislead superiors and the public that something is amiss when really there is no underlying issue of significance interfering with the delivery of good public services except the wretched public servant who was wrongfully placed in the leadership position for which they were not qualified to handle.

Obviously, there had been a conspiracy operating to ruin Redhawk's reputation as an individual and as a professional, to take away 33 years of retirement benefits by concocting some scheme—fabricating some scenarios in terms of job performance, and downright lying to make it all happen. The Coterie put an "*operative*" in place to handle this piece of dirty work.

There are no depths to which jealousy and envy will not plunge in order to spread poisonous misery to others. The Coterie, Servicious, and Cleopatra's provocative acts brought emotions to the surface that could have, had Redhawk been undisciplined, caused severe detriment to all players. They didn't realize they weren't just pitting themselves against what they assumed to be a lone, helpless individual; they were picking a battle with a 33-year foundation of some of the finest people on the face of the Earth. People like many who spoke at public forums and champi- oned causes for the betterment of society, specifically, Kinder County society. People who volunteered on Boards and fueled civic and religious organizations. And just good citizens in general. These individuals and groups had been Redhawk's mainstay for three decades. They were part of Redhawk's salvation, with her ultimate salvation being her relationship with God. She was grateful to God for having placed her in the position that allowed her to be a *"servant leader."* Knowing God and living in the safety and security of His Almighty Presence had sustained Redhawk through many trials. This one was no different.

CELEBRATION

Once Redhawk's intent to retire was publicly announced nearly two months prior to the actual retirement date, Department of Alliance Activity staff, even though saddened by the announcement, got busy preparing for a bedazzling send-off. The retirement celebration that was being planned for Redhawk had a flair of class, style, and professionalism. There was also a monumental show of support from the Kind- er County community. Everyone wondered how the DAA staff had been able to arrange to have the Nation's Number one Sheriff, Christopher Snow, serve as Master of Ceremony at Redhawk's retirement celebration. Rehawk was exhilarated by his appearance on what would be one of the most memorable days of her work life. In his usual fashion, Sheriff Snow wowed the crowd with his quick wit and fantastic humor. With Sheriff Christopher Snow running the show, it's no wonder that the event unfolded and succeeded with Hollywood-style smoothness.

There had not been a similar event in Kinder County that was ever so impeccably choreographed, eclectic, limpid, ebullient—so unlike the facile retirement events of the past. DAA staff wanted to ensure that this would be the best day of Redhawk's life in seven months. On the day of the event, they wanted to be assured that the warmth generated in the gymnasium—where they would be holding the event—would be infectious. Should there be anyone on the scene not having an enjoyable time, their failure to reach what was hoped to be the prevailing scintillating height of excitement, would go undetected.

When the day came, it was one of the most exciting and touching retirement celebrations Kinder County had witnessed in many, many years. More than 400 friends, Xenolina State Officials, local officials, DAA Directors from other counties, Kinder County employees, and county residents were in attendance. All of Redhawk's family who lived in the area attended. Redhawk's daughter, Sheba Hawk, a psychologist employed at Corcoran Prison in California, was unable to attend due to professional obligations with dates that conflicted with the date of the Retirement Celebration. Redhawk's spouse, Jay Hawk, and grandson, Strafield and his father, Vichon, were there celebrating with the crowd. Everyone showered Redhawk with a send-off fit for a queen. DAA staff performed a rendition of the song "New York, New York," and named their soon to be ex-boss *"Queen of the Hill."*

During the celebration, many of Redhawk's colleagues and co-workers bestowed accolades upon her—reminiscing about their years of collaborating as partners. Redhawk was recognized with numerous awards, the most prestigious of which was the *"Blue Bird Award"* from the Governor of the State of Xenolina *"in recognition of dedication and outstanding service as an exemplary employee of the Great State of Xenolina."*

When it was Redhawk's shining moment to speak at the gathering, she expressed apprecia- tion to everyone for helping create many long-last- ing memories. She said her career in public service had been, and continues to be, one of the highlights in her résumé of life. She said retirement could be compared to taking a gargantuan step into an abyss of unknowns. In a written summary statement that she shared with all guests, she thanked God for the desire to serve, and for equipping her with the tools neces- sary for serving with compassion. She thanked God for fortitude and long-standing performance,   which is truly a favor from God.

Additionally, she stated that she was truly grateful for having served for many years with staff, colleagues, clients, and citizens of Kinder County. She told everyone that she was not retiring per the usual definition of retirement. She offered that she was only shifting gears.

Finally, Redhawk stated that she was overwhelmed with joy from the love that had been shown. She thanked everyone for the cards, gifts, and kind words spoken that day. When she closed the curtains and turned the corner, she could be heard talking to the wind saying, that she had heard a rumor that some of Kinder County's decent folk were organizing for the next election, and were planning to *"Drain the Swamp. Then maybe one day Kinder County would truly become a kinder county"*!

EPILOGUE

Writing the book has been a quintessential reminder to embrace each moment of life to the fullest—even when considering and encapsulating the offensive tactics of unknown adversaries, life is still good. Our daily lives don't always flow as we plan because a higher power holds the controls.

Writing this book has enabled me to gain a better understanding of how bitterness can move one in the wrong direction, take one down the wrong path in life, all because self-discipline eludes them at a time when they should be holding steadfastly to the principles that teach us, without hesitation or limitations, to do the right thing. Considering all the tragedies, disasters, and horrific events that occur daily throughout the world, large or small contemptible acts against one another, in the global scheme of things, are miniscule.

Writing this book has been a reminder that if we fail to pay close attention to ourselves, we can begin to self-destruct if we allow ourselves to become entangled in the negative webs that other people attempt to weave in our lives to bring about our demise solely for their own warped sense of power.

Life behooves everyone to overcome serious and unexpected disruptions or vicissitudes of normal daily, weekly, or monthly routines with grace, grit, and gratitude—leaving the final outcome to a higher power—knowing that whatever happened wasn't a worst-case scenario. Because if it had been, chances are we would not be around to read or write about it.

In order to fortify some of our own needs for a certain degree of power and control, affirmation and importance, and intimacy and delight, we must employ a number of self-care strategies to ensure that our thirsts and hungers do not cloud our thinking to the extent that we forget to exercise self-control in our personal lives.

Some individual self-care strategies to reinvigorate mind and body include: (a) Making a regular schedule of *"alone time"* for meditation; (b) Taking short periodic breaks from everything and everyone; (c) Taking long walks; (d) Getting adequate sleep; (e) Maintaining a healthy, wholesome diet; (f) Conferring with a *confidante* when necessary; (g) Keeping at least monthly, one *"play date"*–movie, dinner, dancing, golfing, etc.—with a special someone; (h) Engaging in community activities with your family support system, spiritual leaders, and friends; (i) Preserving a sense of purpose; and (j) "Getting on the balcony."

The contents of this book reflect my repudiation of the Coterie, Shady Worm, Cleopatra, and May Rhinestone as people worthy of respect. They do not respect diverse values, beliefs, and cultures. Their ethical standards appear to be perverted. There is a lot hidden under the sly smiles they parade around Kinder County. There are no rational explanations for irrational acts, and in this story, those people act- ed irrationally when they sequestered an employee from Department of Alliance Activity staff and clients without reason while continuing to pay that employee's salary, although they had forbidden the employee's return to the job. It was all very difficult to assimilate because the employee had worked for pay since she was 8 years old. Paying someone not to work is, and will always be, a real waste of taxpayer dollars when the employee is a highly trained public servant, knowledgeable, and qualified for the position held.

This, in my opinion, cannot be justified—unless, of course, the employer has something to hide.

During the ordeal described herein, it took all the inner strength that could be mustered to quell the fury that was running through my veins in order to stay focused on the beautiful sphere of life. It was gut-wrenching to have been accused of "*something,*" and being totally unaware of what it was. But a *trucu- lent harridan* was out to destroy me for whatever reasons. Escape was virtually impossible when she was being guided and directed by the Coterie and Servicious, whose references to me were always acerbic in nature. They were known throughout Kinder County for their perfidy. So, deep down I should not have been surprised by their actions.

Writing this book was extremely empowering. It drew on my strength and determination to travel the road I have chosen in life, versus wallowing down the path that others have tried to pave for me.

While it was painful to witness Kinder County officials in control and in office to serve the people fighting advocacy for the low-income population, the fight, from my perspective was worth it, and I am gratified by having had the experience. But most of all, I am grateful to God for having given me the opportunity to serve mankind. I hope this book will inspire others with similar experiences to fight to expose violations of policies and laws and unfair treatment.

Even though episodes of the past 18 months caused a sudden change to the landscape of my life, today, like Kintsugi, certain parts of my life are more beautiful for having been broken, and much stronger for having been reinforced by this unfortunate experience.

NOTES FROM DAA STAFF, FRIENDS, AND FB FRIENDS

--Mrs. May, Sunday School Superintendent, called upon everyone for a special prayer at the end of a lesson one Sunday. Pastor Hand prayed for Redhawk's peace of mind and God's guidance and deliverance. She also prayed for the perpetrators of evil and discrimination.

--The Lord promises that those who rule with evilness shall face "night without vision, darkness without revelation." The sun shall go down over them and blackness shall befall them. (Mich 3:6). *Note sent from a friend.*

--Leaders must not condone or ignore injustices for bribes or favor. *Note from a friend.*

--My prayers are that whatever actions you take, the outcome will be favorable. *Note from a Department of Alliance Activity staff member.*

--When are you coming back? It's been four months now! It seems that they were looking for an excuse to be rid of you. *Note from a DAA staff member.*

--She who cannot forgive, burns the bridge over which she, herself, must pass. *Note from a pastor with whom Redhawk was not familiar.*

--Are you the only one in Kinder County Government who has to be perfect? *Question from a Kinder County employee in another department.*

--They searched and searched and the only thing they found was themselves in the mirror looking like a band of fools! *Note from another public official.*

--What can I do to help? *"If I cannot do great things, I can do small things in a great way."—Dr. Martin Luther King Jr.* Just let me know if you need me. *Note from a friend.*

--This is not a tsunami; it's only a wave. *Note from a friend.*

--I don't feel your job is in jeopardy. Keep the faith! *Note from a retired State Official.*

--I hope they won't do anything against the Department of Alliance Activity staff. They are mainly out to get you. *Note from a retired government employee.*

--What comes around, goes around...and treat others as you would like to be treated. God is definitely watching all of them! *Note from a friend who knows them better than I.*

--You showed great concern with me when my first child, a son, was born, and I will always treasure that. You have been a true supporter of all DAA employees also. *Note from a DAA employee.*

--Don't let those devils stress you out, Woman of God! *Note from a friend.*

--Remember you are a warrior! *Note from a friend.*

--Consider who is scheming against you. LOL! (smiley face) *Note from a FBF.*

--Hang in there and do God's work until he decides that you should do something different. *Note from a FBF.*

--They are crazy! They make you lose your religion! *Notes from a FBF.*

--Did you know I was given a written warning

for NOTHING three days after you left? *Note from a FBF.*

--So honored that you passed your tough skin of leadership through Kinder County. I learned so much from you about successful civic duty. *Note from a leading Kinder County Baptist Minister.*

--Thank you for always being there for us! *Note from a Department of Alliance Activity staff member.*

--The best is yet to come for you. Lots of love and prayers. *Note from a leading Kinder County Methodist Minister.*

--Begin each day by giving thanks to God for his Grace and Mercy. He will take care of you. *Note from a friend.*

--Have they forgotten that people push back when you disturb their equilibrium? *Note from a DAA Director from another Xenolina county.*

--You were always in their line of fire because you would always tell them what they needed to hear rather than what they wanted to hear. *Note from a retired member of the Coterie.*

--They don't understand that leadership is not synonymous with socializing. LOL! *Note from a FBF.*

--People criticize you when they don't like the message. *Note from a retired member of the Coterie.*

--In your position, you have to bear the pain and scars of people saying awful things about you. *Note from a DAA Director from another Xenolina county.*

--Through all of this, take care of yourself! *Note from a friend.*

--While this time in your life may be painful, in the end you will know it was worth it. God does not make mistakes. *Note from a friend.*

--Trials, temptations, disappointments—all of these are inspirations instead of hindrances if one uses the rightly. They not only test our fiber of character, but strengthen it. Remember: You can't have message without a MESS or a testimony without a TEST. Let what was meant to break you...make you! –Unknown. *Note from a FBF.*

--"How people treat you is their karma; how you react is yours."--*Dr. Wayne Dyer. Note from my sister.*

--Every time you wake up, ask yourself, "What good things am I going to do today"? Remember when the sun goes down at sunset, it will take a part of your life with it. --*Native American Proverb. Note from my cousin.*

--Three things you cannot recover in life: The word after it's said, the moment after it's missed, and time after it's gone. So chose words wisely, embrace every moment we have with those we love, and never waste time in any way—not arguing because whatever the debate is, it won't matter in the final moments of life. *Note from my FBF Amanda.*

--The best thing about the past is it shows us what not to bring into our future. *Note from a FBF.*

--Never blame anyone for your life. People are just people. Some will add to your happiness and others will test your patience. In the end, it's your response that decides the value of any experience.— *Jonathan Wells. Note from a cousin.*

--Life is too ironic to fully understand it. It takes experiencing sadness to know what happiness is. Noise to appreciate silence, and absence to value presence. *Note from a FBF.*

--I think this is clear to everyone that this is personal with Cleopatra. *Note from a DAA Director from another Xenolina County.*

--I know this has left the Coterie with many thoughts as to whether Cleopatra is making them look like fools. *Note from a concerned Kinder County citizen.*

--Shame, too, on the County Keeper! *Note from a friend in an adjoining county.*

--When they can wipe the mud off their faces, I guess they will tell you to come back to work or fire you. *Note from a friend in another state.*

--*"A good character is the best tombstone. Those who loved you, and were helped by you, will remember you when forget-me-nots have withered. Carve your name on hearts, not on marble".—Unknown. Note from a FBF.*

--Show respect—even to people who don't deserve it; not as a reflection of their character, but a reflection of yours. *Note from a FBF.*

--Five things to quit right now: Trying to please everyone. Fearing change. Living in the past. Putting yourself down. Overthinking. *Note from a FBF.*

R. M. Shiver is a native of Rocky Point, N.C. Following her retirement in 2016 from the position of Director of Social Services for Pender County, she used the newly treasured uncommitted time to pen her first book, *Kinder County*. Inspiration for of the book's contents is based on facets of her true-life experiences and the antics of individuals she encountered along her life's journey. She lives near the Northeast Cape Fear River in southeastern North Carolina with family—her spouse of 55 years and her 13-year-old grandson.